CAROL VORDERM
French Made Ea

10 Minutes A Day

French

Ages 7-11

Author and Consultant
Charlotte Tomson

This timer counts up to 10 minutes.
When it reaches 10:00 it will beep.

How to use the timer:
Switch the timer ON.
Press the triangle ▶ to START the timer.
Press the square ■ to STOP or PAUSE the timer.
Press the square ■ to RESET the timer to 00:00.
Press any button to WAKE UP the timer.

Penguin
Random
House

Senior Editor Cécile Landau
Editor Nishtha Kapil
Asst. Editor Kritika Gupta
Senior Art Editor Ann Cannings
Project Art Editor Tanvi Nathyal
Art Editor Roohi Rais
French Consultant Charlotte Tomson
DTP Designer Anita Yadav
Managing Editor Soma B. Chowdhury
Managing Art Editor Ahlawat Gunjan
Art Director Martin Wilson
Senior Producer, Pre-Production
Francesca Wardell
Producer Priscilla Reby

First published in Great Britain in 2016 by
Dorling Kindersley Limited
80 Strand, London, WC2R 0RL

Copyright © 2016 Dorling Kindersley Limited
A Penguin Random House Company
10 9 8 7 6 5 4 3
004–285396–Jan/2016

A CIP catalogue record for this book
is available from the British Library.
ISBN: 978-0-2412-2517-2

Printed and bound in China.

All images © Dorling Kindersley Limited
For further information see: www.dkimages.com

A WORLD OF IDEAS:
SEE ALL THERE IS TO KNOW
www.dk.com

Contents

Time taken

Time filler:
In these boxes are some extra challenges to extend your skills. You can do them if you have some time left after finishing the questions and continue until you hear the 10-minute beep. Or, these can be stand-alone activities that you can do in 10 minutes.

Bonjour! Ça va?

Practise speaking French by introducing yourself, greeting other people and saying how you are. Press the timer. **Vas-y!**

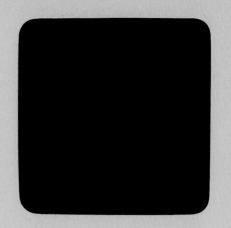

1 **Bonjour** means "hello" and the more informal **salut** can be translated as "hi". Write the best greeting for each of these people.

your friend .... a policeman ....

your teacher .... your mother ....

2 Here are three French expressions that you might use to say how you feel. Draw lines to match each one to a picture below.

Ça ne va pas.   **Ça va comme ci, comme ça.**   **Ça va bien, merci.**

3 To be polite, use **monsieur** (sir), **madame** (madam) and **mademoiselle** (miss) with your greetings. Say **au revoir** (goodbye) politely to the people in these pictures.

....

Time filler:
Write down the names of some of your friends. Use the internet to check if there is a French equivalent of each name. Practise greeting your friends in French, using equivalent French names where possible.

---

4 Here are two ways of asking "What is your name?" in French, but the vowels are missing. Add the vowels to complete each sentence.

C___mm___nt t___ t'___pp___ll___s?

C___mm___nt t'___pp___ll___s-t___?

---

5 Match each French name with its English equivalent.

Stéphanie   **Éléonore**   **Étienne**   **Édouard**   **Pierre**

Stephen   Stephanie   Peter   Eleanor   Edward

---

6 Translate each phrase from English to French. Use the French equivalent of people's names.

Goodbye, Stephen!   ....

My name is Edward.   ....

How are you, Peter?   ....

---

7 The words in these greetings are all mixed up. Unscramble them and write each sentence correctly.

Ça va merci. bien, ...

t'appelles-tu? Comment   ....

madame! Bonjour, ...

Les nombres 1–20

When learning the numbers in any language, it is best to practise them in groups of ten or twenty. Try saying them backwards. Have a go at counting from a random number.

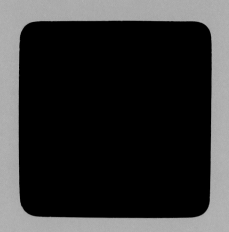

1 A rocket is about to be launched. Below is the countdown in French, but some of the numbers are missing. Fill in the gaps.

dix, neuf,_____, sept,_____,_____,

quatre,_____,_____,_____,

zéro! Feu!

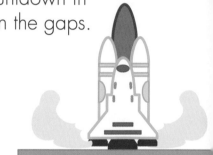

2 Write the number for each French number word.

un	____	deux	____	quatre	____
sept	____	huit	____	dix	____
onze	____	douze	____	treize	____
quinze	____	dix-sept	____	vingt	____

3 Complete each calculation in French.

dix + sept = _____   huit + deux = _____

cinq + sept = _____   douze – un = _____

trois x deux = _____   vingt – cinq = _____

4 Circle the words that have silent last letters.

un   deux   trois   cinq   sept

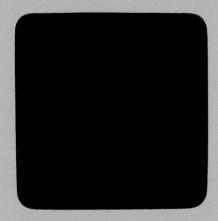

Time filler:
Shuffle a pack of playing cards and then place it face down. Take the top card, turn it over and say the number on it aloud in French. Repeat until you have gone through all the cards. If you pick a Jack, Queen or King, move on to the next card.

5 Translate each number into French. Then complete the crossword.

Across

1. two ....
2. eight ....
3. nine ....
4. thirteen ....
5. twenty ....

Down

1. eleven ....
2. twelve ....
3. three ....
4. ten ....
5. seven ....

8

Ma famille

These exercises will give you plenty of practice at using the words you will need to describe your family and your friends' families.

1. Read the information given in the chart below. Then use it to write the name of the child shown in each picture.

Je m'appelle Thomas. J'ai une sœur et un frère.	Je m'appelle Sophie. J'ai deux frères.
Je m'appelle Juliette. J'ai une sœur. Je n'ai pas de frère.	Je m'appelle Frédéric. Je n'ai ni frères ni sœurs.

....

....

....

....

2. Translate these phrases. Remember to use the correct French word for "my" (**mon, ma** or **mes**) in each case.

my brother ....   my mother ....

my grandmother ....   my sisters ....

Time filler:
Write a brief description of everyone in your family, or of each of your friends, in French. Use a dictionary to help you.

(3) Look at the people in this family. Then complete each sentence.

Le père s'appelle .... La mère s'appelle ....

Le grand-père s'appelle .... La grand-mère s'appelle ....

Le petit garcon s'appelle .... La sœur s'appelle ....

Les bébés s'appellent ....

Les enfants s'appellent ....

(4) Circle the correct form of the verb **s'appeler** in each sentence.

Mes frères s'appelle / s'appellent Adrien et Charles.

La sœur de David s'appelle / s'appellent Élisabeth.

Mes parents s'appelle / s'appellent Louis et Marie.

Quel âge as-tu?

In French, we use the verb **avoir** (to have) to say how old we are. For example, to say that you are nine years old in French, you would say, **"J'ai neuf ans."**

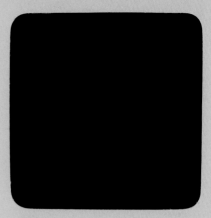

(1) Look at each picture. Then complete each sentence by writing the missing word.

J'ai .... ans.

J'ai .... ans.

J'ai .... ans.

J'ai .... ans.

J'ai .... ans.

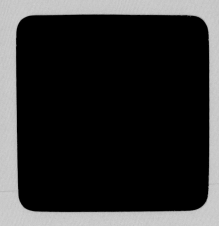

Time filler:
Write down the ages of your friends and members of your family. Then practise saying in French how old each one of them is. You could also write down the French sentences you use, if you have time.

2 Here is a sheet from a notebook, showing the names and ages of some children taken on a school trip. Next to it, write sentences in French, stating each child's age. The first one has been done for you.

Prénom	Age
Pierre	7
Édouard	11
Mustafa	9
Stéphanie	8
Luc	10
Christelle	12

Pierre a sept ans.

3 Fill in the missing letters to complete each sentence.

Ma sœ__r a qu__re ans.

M__n frè__ a n__uf a__s.

J'a__ s__pt an__.

J'ai o__e __ns.

4 Translate these sentences into French.

He is ten.

She is eight years old.

He is fourteen.

She is three.

Dans mon cartable

In French, all nouns are either masculine or feminine. Also, the French words for "a/an" (**un** and **une**) and "the" (**le**, **la** or **les**) vary depending on whether the noun following them is masculine or feminine.

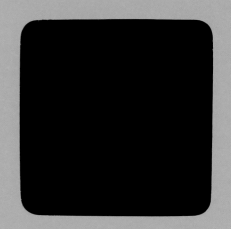

1 Fill in the chart. Add the French word for each object listed in English, as well as the correct French word for "the" (**le**, **la** or **les**) that you would use in each case. **Note:** You may use a dictionary to help you.

English	le, la or les	French
pencil		
pen		
rubber		
pencil case		
calculator		
felt-tip pen		
pencil sharpener		
school bag		
notebook		
ruler		

2 Circle the correct French word for "a/an" in each phrase.

un / une sac   un / une règle

un / une gomme   un / une crayon

un / une stylo   un / une trousse

un / une feutre   un / une calculatrice

un / une cahier   un / une taille-crayon

Time filler
Empty out your school bag. Write a description of the contents, using a dictionary to look up any new word. Start by writing: **Dans mon cartable, j'ai...** (In my school bag, I have...).

---

3) The following sentence is written as a code.

11 4 1 23   18 15 1   26 4 6 9 4 17 2 7,   20' 4 14 25 1   23 9 13 2 15.

Use this code-breaking chart to reveal what letter each number in the coded sentence stands for. Then write the decoded message.

a	b	c	d	e	i	j	l	m	n	o	r	s	t	u	y
4	17	26	11	7	14	20	2	18	1	15	6	23	9	25	13

....

---

4) Find the French words for ten classroom objects in this word-search puzzle.
Hint: All the words can be found on the chart on page 12.

s	p	u	f	x	f	t	r	o	u	s	s	e
t	a	i	l	l	e	-	c	r	a	y	o	n
y	z	f	c	m	u	h	f	è	i	p	h	a
l	e	r	x	n	t	i	r	g	t	j	p	g
o	b	q	z	s	r	c	d	l	w	c	r	o
e	i	w	p	l	e	l	g	e	s	a	e	m
l	o	u	c	r	a	y	o	n	v	h	t	m
l	c	a	l	c	u	l	a	t	r	i	c	e
b	u	f	p	a	i	i	g	o	z	e	a	h
c	a	r	t	a	b	l	e	a	t	r	b	c

Les nombres 20–69

Remember that with numbers over 20, when just one unit is added to the tens, the French say **vingt et un** (twenty and one), **trente et un** (thirty and one) and so on, to make pronunciation easier.

1 Complete each number word in the chart.

Number	Number word
23	vingt- ....
34	.... -quatre
41	quarante et ....
52	.... -deux
69	soixante- ....

2 Write these numbers as digits.

trente et un ☐   soixante-sept ☐   vingt-quatre ☐

vingt-six ☐   cinquante-huit ☐   quarante-neuf ☐

3 Write the French for each number.

51 ....   42 ....   63 ....

29 ....   35 ....   57 ....

4 Write the next two numbers in each sequence.

vingt et un, vingt-deux, ...

quarante-six, quarante-sept, ...

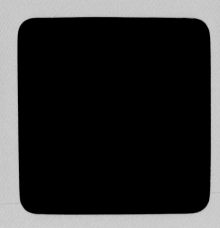

Time filler:
Look around your home. Look in books
and magazines, at pictures and clocks.
Write down any number you see between
20 and 69. Then write the French word for
each of these numbers.

5) Solve these sums. Write the answers, first in digits and then in French.

3 x 7 = ☐ ....   6 x 7 = ☐ ....

9 x 3 = ☐ ....   12 x 3 = ☐ ....

6 x 8 = ☐ ....   10 x 5 = ☐ ....

8 x 8 = ☐ ....   11 x 5 = ☐ ....

7 x 9 = ☐ ....   11 x 3 = ☐ ....

6) In this word-search puzzle, find the French words for the ten numbers that
are answers to the sums in question 5.

c	i	n	q	u	a	n	t	e	-	c	i	n	q	f	t
e	r	t	u	i	p	w	r	p	f	y	q	u	t	w	r
q	u	a	r	a	n	t	e	-	h	u	i	t	r	e	e
r	t	y	u	p	v	i	n	g	t	-	s	e	p	t	n
s	q	u	a	r	a	n	t	e	-	d	e	u	x	p	t
s	o	i	x	a	n	t	e	-	q	u	a	t	r	e	e
t	u	v	i	n	x	t	-	e	t	l	u	n	e	f	-
c	i	n	t	e	v	i	s	e	p	h	u	t	r	e	t
i	m	i	e	g	h	c	i	n	q	u	a	n	t	e	r
n	a	h	t	r	u	i	x	p	l	e	a	h	u	i	o
s	o	i	x	a	n	t	e	-	t	r	o	i	s	t	i
q	u	a	v	i	n	g	t	e	t	u	n	u	x	w	s

Les mois

Unlike in English, the names of the months in French begin with a small letter – for example, **juin** (June).

(1) Select French words for the months of the year from the chart below to match the list of months in English.

août	janvier	septembre	mars	novembre	avril
février	mai	juin	octobre	décembre	juillet

January ....

February ....

March ....

April ....

May ....

June ....

July ....

August ....

September ....

October ....

November ....

December ....

(2) Use the first letter and the number of spaces provided as clues to work out the birthday month of each child.

Mon anniversaire est le 26 j ....

Mon anniversaire est le 17 a ....

Mon anniversaire est le 10 f ....

Mon anniversaire est le 31 a ....

Time filler:
Make your own French calendar. Divide a large sheet of paper into twelve equal sections and label each section with the name of a month in French. Record important dates and events on your calendar in French, too!

③ Quelle est la date de ton anniversaire?
When is your birthday?

....

④ The letters have fallen out of the bottom of this puzzle grid! On the way down, they got mixed up, although they are still in their correct rows. Unscramble them to discover the mystery birthday date.

```
        o   n   m
  e   a   i   r   s   v   e   r   n   i   n   a
        s   t   l   e   e
  u   n   t   g   i   n   e   t   v
  m   e   e   t   b   p   r   s   e
```

⑤ Continue this sequence.

mars   avril   mai   ....

Les adjectifs

In French, adjectives must be in their masculine form when they are used to describe a masculine noun and in their feminine form when used to describe a feminine noun.

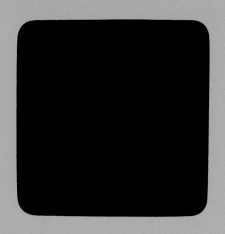

1 Write the feminine form and the English translation for each adjective listed on the chart. **Note:** You may use a dictionary to help you.

French (Masculine)	French (Feminine)	English
gentil		
timide		
gourmand		
petit		
grand		
sportif		
méchant		
beau		
paresseux		
mignon		
marrant		
sympa		

2 Complete the following sentences using adjectives from the chart above.

Je suis .... et ....

Ma mère est .... et ....

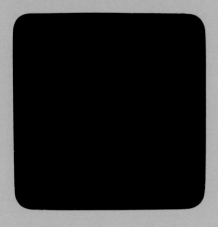

Time filler:
Practise your French by describing your family or friends. What do they look like? What are their main characteristics? Remember to make the adjectives you use agree with the gender of the person that you are describing.

3 Choose your favourite character from a book or a film. Write a few sentences describing him or her in French.

....

....

....

....

4 Circle the adjective in each French sentence that correctly matches the English sentences.

He has brown hair.	Il a les cheveux bruns / roux / blonds / noirs.
She has red hair.	Elle a les cheveux bruns / roux / blonds / noirs.
He has green eyes.	Il a les yeux marron / bleus / verts / gris.
She has blue eyes.	Elle a les yeux marron / bleus / verts / gris.

5 Write a brief description of yourself in French. Use **Je suis**… (I am…) and **J'ai**… (I have…) to begin your sentences.

....

....

....

....

Beat the clock 1

Write the correct present tense form
of the verbs shown in brackets below.
Remember that they are all regular verbs,
ending in **-er**. How many can you do in
10 minutes? **Vas-y!**

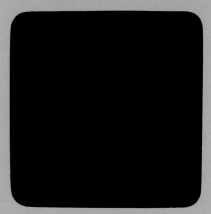

Je (parler) ....

Elle (arriver) ....

Tu (donner) ....

Il (habiter) ....

Il (arriver) ....

Tu (parler) ....

Nous (parler) ....

Vous (manger) ....

Ils (donner) ....

Ils (arriver) ....

Elle (habiter) ....

Ils (habiter) ....

Je (manger) ....

Tu (aimer) ....

Nous (aimer) ....

Vous (parler) ....

Je (regarder) ....

Tu (regarder) ....

Il (travailler) ....

Il (jouer) ....

Tu (jouer) ....

Tu (écouter) ....

Elle (donner) ....

Tu (travailler) ....

Nous (écouter) ....

Vous (aimer) ....

Elles (habiter) ....

Je (jouer) ....

Time filler:
Translate each infinitive verb in the list below into English. Keep testing yourself on these verbs – their meaning and present tense. They are used frequently in French and you will need to be familiar with them.

Il (parler) ....

Je (donner) ....

Nous (donner) ....

Il (donner) ....

Tu (arriver) ....

Elle (aimer) ....

Vous (habiter) ....

Elle (parler) ....

Il (aimer) ....

Vous (arriver) ....

Il (regarder) ....

Elles (aimer) ....

Elle (jouer) ....

Tu (habiter) ....

Elles (parler) ....

Ils (parler) ....

Nous (habiter) ....

Vous (donner) ....

Je (travailler) ....

Elle (regarder) ....

Il (écouter) ....

Nous (jouer) ....

Ils (aimer) ....

Il (manger) ....

Elles (donner) ....

Vous (écouter) ....

Nous (arriver) ....

Elles (arriver) ....

22

Les couleurs

French words for colours must be written in their masculine, feminine or plural form, depending on the gender of the noun they are describing and whether it is singular or plural.

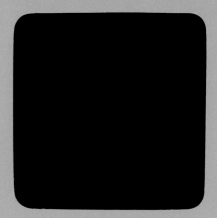

① Translate the English colour words into French.

red

yellow

black

....

....

....

grey

orange

blue

....

....

....

brown

violet

green

....

....

....

② Unscramble these French colour words.

canbl ....

georu ....

reogan ....

romran ....

trev ....

uneja ....

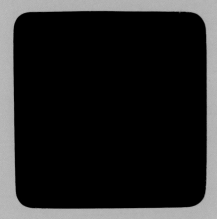

3 Fill in the chart by writing the different French forms of each colour given in English.

English	French (Masculine/Plural)	French (Feminine/Plural)
red		
yellow		
blue		
green		
brown		
orange		
white		
black		
grey		
violet		
pink		

4 Spot the mistakes! Write each phrase using the correct form of the adjective.

une gomme violete ....

des crayons marrons ....

un chapeau rouges ....

ma robe blanc ....

Les jours de la semaine

Remember that days (and months) in French start with a small letter – unlike in English, where they have an initial capital letter.

1 Draw a line linking each day in French to its English equivalent.

mardi	Sunday
samedi	Monday
jeudi	Tuesday
lundi	Wednesday
mercredi	Thursday
dimanche	Friday
vendredi	Saturday

2 Continue each sequence.

mardi ....

vendredi ....

dimanche ....

mercredi ....

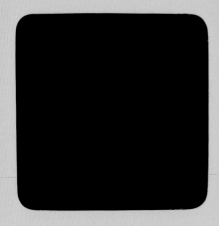

3 Complete these sentences.

Avant mardi, c'est ....

Après samedi, c'est ....

Avant vendredi, c'est ....

Après lundi, c'est ....

lundi

mardi

mercredi

jeudi

vendredi

samedi

dimanche

4 Translate the following dates into French.

Monday, 3rd July ....

Saturday, 1st September ....

Wednesday, 5th January ....

5 Answer the questions in French.

What is the date tomorrow? ....

What was the date yesterday? ....

What will the date be
in two days time? ....

Les animaux

Talking about animals is a good way to practise expressing yourself in French. Watch out for some irregular plurals!

(1) In each pair, circle the smaller animal. Use a dictionary to look up any word that you do not know.

un chien	un éléphant
un chat	un tigre
un cheval	une souris
un oiseau	un gorille
un lapin	une abeille
une grenouille	un mouton

(2) Unscramble the sentences below.

chiens. a deux Pierre

Sophie trois a chevaux.

a quatre David oiseaux.

(3) Which animals do you prefer? Answer in full sentences.

Tu préfères les chats ou les chiens?

Tu préfères les tortues ou les poissons rouges?

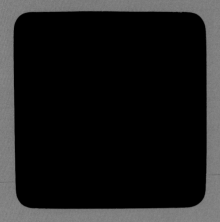

Time filler:
Create a poster for your ideal zoo or
animalerie (pet shop). Label the animals
in French. Write a short paragraph describing
how many there are of each kind of animal.
Start with **Il y a...** (There are...).

(4) Work out which animal is making the sounds.

miaou

Quel animal fait miaou?

....

Quel animal fait coin-coin?

....

coin-coin

cocorico

Quel animal fait cocorico?

....

Quel animal fait ouah-ouah?

....

ouah-ouah

(5) Read out the list of animals in the box below.

la grenouille   la vache   le mouton   le tigre   le canard   le gorille

Now sort the animals by where you are most likely to see each one.

dans le lac?   à la ferme?   dans le zoo?

....

....

La maison

Help yourself learn the French words for the various rooms in your house by placing flash cards showing the words on walls and doors.

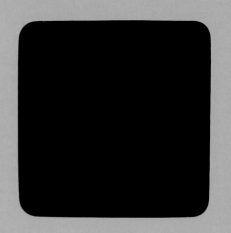

(1) Translate these words into English. **Note**: You may use a dictionary to help you.

le salon	....	le bureau	....
le grenier	....	le sous-sol	....
la cuisine	....	la salle de bains	....
la chambre	....	la salle à manger	....
l'escalier	....	le jardin	....
la cave	....	la chambre d'enfants	....

(2) Look at these lists of things you might find in some of the rooms in your house. Circle the object in each list that would be out of place.

La cuisine:
l'évier
l'oreiller
le frigo
le four

Le salon:
l'évier
le sofa
les rideaux
le fauteuil

La chambre:
le lit
le tapis
l'oreiller
le four

La salle de bains:
la douche
le lavabo
le lit
la serviette

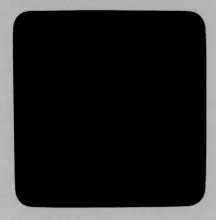

Time filler:
Write a description of your house. Start your sentences with **Au sous-sol**, **il y a...** (In the basement, there is...), **Au rez-de-chaussée**, **il y a...** (On the ground floor, there is...), **Au premier étage**, **il y a...** (On the first floor, there is...), and so on.

3 Look at the picture. Then answer the questions below in French.

Qu'est-ce qu'il y a au rez-de-chaussée?

....

....

Qu'est-ce qu'il y a au premier étage?

....

....

Qu'est-ce qu'il y a au deuxième étage?

....

....

Où habites-tu?

What sort of house do you live in? What is the name of your town or village? What type of location do you live in? Can you remember when to use **à, en** or **dans** to translate the word "in" in "live in"?

(1) Complete the chart by adding the English translations.

French	English
une maison	
un appartement	
une maison jumelée	
une maison individuelle	
une maison mitoyenne	
un bungalow	

(2) Find out what the French expressions mean by unscrambling their English translations.

French	English		
en ville	in tnow	=	
à la campagne	in the cidentrouys	=	
en banlieue	in the rbssubu	=	
à la montagne	in the itmounasn	=	
au bord de la mer	by the esa	=	

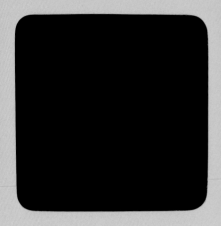

Time filler:
Think of a character from one of your favourite storybooks. Try to describe in French where he or she lives and in what type of house. Is it in the country or in a town? Is it in the mountains or in the woods? Is it near a river or lake, or by the sea?

3 Insert the correct form of the present tense of the verb **habiter** (to live) in these sentences.

J'................................ à Londres.

Il .... au bord de la mer.

Tu .... en banlieue.

Ils .... à la campagne.

Nous .... en ville.

Vous .... dans un village.

4 Translate these French sentences into English.

J'habite avec mes parents dans une maison jumelée.

....

Elle habite avec sa mère dans un grand appartement.

....

5 Translate these English sentences into French.

My grandparents live on an old farm in the mountains.

....

My cousins live in a bungalow by the sea.

....

Les pays

Remember that "in" and "to" translate as **au** before a country name that is masculine in French, as **en** before a country name that is feminine, and as **aux** before a plural country name. But to say "in" or "to" before the name of a city, you use **à**.

1 Translate these sentences from English to French. **Note:** You may use a dictionary to help you.

I live in France.

....

I live by the sea in Greece.

....

I work in the Netherlands.

....

He lives in the mountains in Italy.

....

She lives in Canada.

....

He is going to Wales.

....

I am going to the USA.

....

She lives in Spain.

....

They live in the countryside in Portugal.

....

Time filler:
Look up the French words for various nationalities in a dictionary. Then write the nationalities and the country names associated with them in pairs. Use a capital letter for the country and a lower case letter for the nationality, for example, **Angleterre, anglais**.

(2) Fill in the chart by writing the French name for each country.
Note: You may use a dictionary to help you.

English	French
Scotland	
England	
Ireland	
Belgium	
Germany	
Denmark	
Switzerland	
Turkey	
Norway	

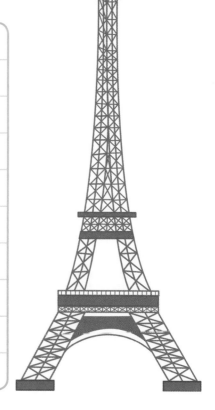

(3) Translate the sentences below from English to French.

I work in London. ....

I am going to Barcelona. ....

I live in Paris. ....

(4) Write the correct French translation for "in" or "to" that you would use before each of these destinations.

.... New York   .... Californie   .... États-Unis

En ville

These exercises will help you learn the French for places around town that you might want to visit, such as shops, museums and restaurants. Pay special attention to the gender of nouns.

(1) Complete the chart by adding the English translations.
Note: You may use a dictionary to help you.

French	English
le supermarché	
la poste	
l'école	
la banque	
le parc	
le musée	
la librairie	
le café	
l'hôpital	
la gare	
la piscine	
le restaurant	

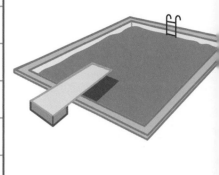

(2) Answer these questions in French.

Où est-ce qu'on achète de la viande? ....

Où est-ce qu'on achète des gâteaux? ....

Où est-ce qu'on achète du pain? ....

Time filler:
Describe your town. Start with the phrase, **Dans ma ville, il y a...** (In my town, there is/are...). You could also practise saying what your town lacks, using the phrase **Il n'y a pas de...** (There is/are no...).

3) Complete this chart by adding the correct form of the present tense of the verb **aller** (to go).

English	French
I go	Je ....
You (singular) go	Tu ....
He/she goes	Il/Elle ....
We go	Nous ....
You (plural) go	Vous ....
They go	Il/Elles ....

4) Choose the right way to say "to" – **au, à la, à l'** or **aux** – to complete the phrases below.

Je vais .... hôtel.

Tu vas .... collège.

Ils vont .... cinéma.

Nous allons .... station-service.

5) Use the right form of the verb **aller** (to go) and the right way of saying "to" to complete the sentences below.

Sophie .... église.

Nous .... magasins.

Il .... hôpital.

Ils .... stade.

Je .... restaurant.

Tu .... banque?

Elles .... coiffeuse.

Mon père .... musée.

Où est...?

Practise asking people for directions in French and listen carefully to the answer to make sure you understand it! Can you describe the location and position of buildings in French?

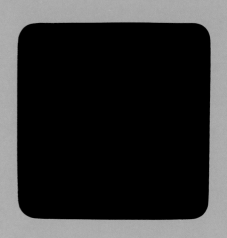

---

(1) Unscramble these sentences to reveal three requests for directions.

je Comment aller peux à gare? la

....

Madame, Pardon aller poste? à la pour

....

Pardon Monsieur, le où est restaurant?

....

---

(2) Draw lines linking the French phrases with their English translations.

en face de   between

près de   opposite

à côté de   near

devant   in front of

entre   behind

derrière   next to

---

(3) Choose from **du**, **de la**, **de l'** or **des** to complete the directions below.

Il y a une poste en face .... gare.

Il y a une banque près .... hôtel.

Il y a un office de tourisme près .... magasins.

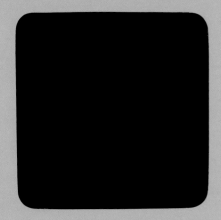

Time filler:
Draw a map of your neighbourhood or local town centre. Label some of the places and buildings in French. Put a dot and write **Tu es ici** (You are here) next to it. Write directions in French from this position to different places on the map.

(4) Translate these English sentences into French.

The bank is between the church and the museum.

....

My school is near my house and the park.

....

The bookshop is next to the café and the station.

....

(5) Look at these symbols for various directions.

Allez tout droit   Tournez à droite   Tournez à gauche

Prenez la deuxième
rue à droite

Prenez la première
rue à gauche

Now write in French what the sequences of symbols below mean:

....

....

....

38

Le temps libre

Remember that you use **faire de** when you want to say that you "do" any activity, but you use **jouer à** when you want to say that you "play" a sport.

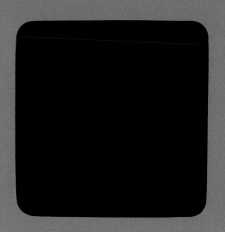

1) Fill in the chart by ticking (✔) the correct column to say which of the sports listed is masculine or feminine, and adding the English translation.
Note: You may use a dictionary to help you.

French	Masculine	Feminine	English
tennis			
foot			
équitation			
natation			
gymnastique			
vélo			
planche à voile			

2) Use the correct form of **faire de** to complete the sentences below.
Remember: de changes to **du, de la** or **de l'**, depending on whether the French word for the activity following it is masculine or feminine.

Je _____ _____ ski.

Nous _____ _____ équitation.

Tu _____ _____ natation.

Il _____ _____ gymnastique.

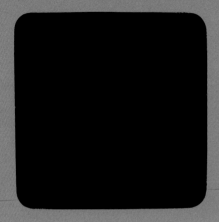

Time filler:
Design a timetable for your own leisure centre.
Label each column with a day of the week:
lundi, **mardi**, **mercredi**, and so on.
Under each day, list the sports and other
activities on offer.

3 Write the correct form of **jouer à** or **faire de** to complete each sentence.

Elles .... skate.

Tu .... tennis.

Nous .... foot.

Je .... natation.

Il .... gymnastique.

Vous .... équitation.

4 Write about which sports you like and which you dislike by completing the following sentences.

J'aime ....

Je n'aime pas ....

J'adore ....

Je détèste ....

Mon sport préféré, c'est ....

5 Choose the correct verb from the box below to complete the sentences.

écouter	aller	faire	lire

J'aime .... au cinéma.

J'aime .... des livres.

J'aime .... les magasins.

J'aime .... de la musique.

Quelle heure est-il?

Practise telling the time in French. Remember that **heure** is a feminine noun, so "one o'clock" will be **une heure** in French and "half past one" will be **une heure et demie**.

① Draw lines to match the time on each clock with the correct sentence.

Il est six heures.   Il est neuf heures.   Il est trois heures.

② Add **et quart**, **et demie** or **moins le quart** to complete the French translations on the chart below.

English	French
It is quarter past two.	Il est deux heures ....
It is quarter past one.	Il est une heure ....
It is half past five.	Il est cinq heures ....
It is half past four.	Il est quatre heures ....
It is quarter to ten.	Il est dix heures ....
It is quarter to eleven.	Il est onze heures ....

③ Unscramble these English sentences. Then translate them into French.

I'ts madyid.   ....

Its' nhtigmdi.   ....

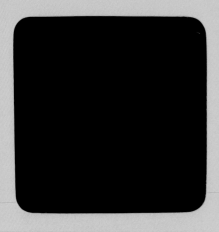

Time filler:
Use simple drawings to show your morning routine – getting up, washing and dressing, having breakfast and brushing your teeth. Under the picture of each activity, write the time that you usually do it in French.

4 Circle the correct sentence to match the time on each clock.

Il est deux heures.   Il est quatre heures moins le quart.

Il est une heure dix.   Il est deux heures moins le quart.

Il est cinq heures.   Il est trois heures moins le quart.

5 Write the time shown on the digital clocks in French.

....

....

6 Answer these questions about how you spend your evening. To say at a specific time, use **à** + the time, for example, **à huit heures** (at eight o'clock).

À quelle heure est-ce que tu fais tes devoirs?

....

À quelle heure est-ce que tu regardes la télévision?

....

Beat the clock 2

Write the correct present tense form of the verbs shown in brackets below. Remember that they are all regular verbs that end in **-ir**. **Vas-y!**

Je (choisir) ....

Tu (finir) ....

Il (réussir) ....

Nous (choisir) ....

Ils (finir) ....

Elle (réfléchir) ....

Je (remplir) ....

Nous (remplir) ....

J' (avertir) ....

Il (obéir) ....

Tu (vieillir) ....

Elle (finir) ....

Nous (établir) ....

Elles (réfléchir) ....

Elle (réussir) ....

Il (réfléchir) ....

Tu (choisir) ....

Je (finir) ....

Ils (réussir) ....

Ils (réfléchir) ....

Tu (remplir) ....

Vous (choisir) ....

Tu (avertir) ....

Il (vieillir) ....

Tu (établir) ....

J' (obéir) ....

Vous (remplir) ....

Je (réussir) ....

Time filler:
Translate each infinitive verb in the list below into English. Keep testing yourself on these verbs – their meaning and present tense. They are used frequently in French and you will need to be familiar with them.

Il (choisir) ....

Nous (finir) ....

Tu (réussir) ....

Vous (réfléchir) ....

Il (remplir) ....

Il (avertir) ....

Elle (vieillir) ....

Elles (choisir) ....

Nous (réfléchir) ....

Tu (obéir) ....

Il (établir) ....

Ils (remplir) ....

Elles (finir) ....

Nous (réussir) ....

Je (réfléchir) ....

Il (finir) ....

Elle (remplir) ....

Elle (choisir) ....

Vous (réussir) ....

Elles (remplir) ....

Tu (réfléchir) ....

Ils (choisir) ....

Vous (finir) ....

Elle (avertir) ....

Nous (vieillir) ....

Il (obéir) ....

Vous (établir) ....

Elles (réussir) ....

Ma routine

When you talk about your daily routine in French, you will use reflexive verbs that describe actions you do to yourself, such as **se réveiller** (to wake up). You may also use adverbs and time-connective words, such as **puis** (then) and **après** (after), to say what order things happen in.

(1) Choose reflexive pronouns from the box below to complete the different forms of the present tense of the verb **se lever** (to get up).

| se | me | te | vous | nous |

Je .... lève   Nous .... levons

Tu .... lèves   Vous .... levez

Il/Elle .... lève   Ils/Elles .... lèvent

(2) Draw lines to match the French sentences about your daily routine to their English translation.

Je me lève.   I wake up.

Je me réveille.   I get dressed.

Je me peigne.   I get up.

Je me douche.   I comb my hair.

Je me couche.   I brush my teeth.

Je m'habille.   I have a shower.

Je me brosse les dents.   I go to bed.

Je prends le déjeuner.   I read a book.

Je lis un livre.   I have lunch.

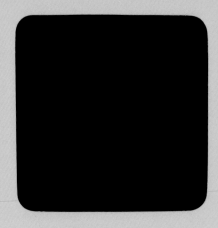

Time filler:
Make a word snake! Ask a friend to write a list in French of what he or she does each morning, but with no spaces between the words. Can you put the spaces in the right places and work out his or her routine?

3 Write the English for these French adverbs. **Note:** You may use a dictionary to help you.

normalement

souvent

de temps en temps

rarement

4 Complete the following sentences by adding an adverb to say how often you do the after-school activities mentioned.

Je lis

Je sors avec mes copains

Je regarde la télé

Je fais mes devoirs

J'écoute de la musique

5 Read the paragraph in French below. Underline the time-connective words and phrases.

Premièrement, je me réveille. Je me lève d'habitude cinq minutes plus tard. Puis, je me lave, je m'habille et je prends mon petit déjeuner. Après ça, je me brosse les dents. Finalement, je me peigne.

Les vêtements

Watch out here for words such as **jean** (jeans), **pantalon** (trousers), **pyjama** (pyjamas) and **short** (shorts), which are plural in English, but singular in French!

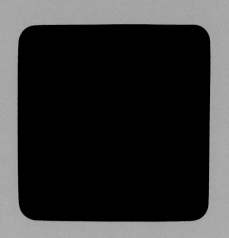

1 Fill the gaps on the chart below. Use a dictionary to look up new words.

French	English
un pantalon	
un jean	
	a T-shirt
un chemisier	
un manteau	
un chapeau	
	some pyjamas
un short	

French	English
une chemise	
	a dress
	a skirt
une écharpe	
des gants	
des chaussettes	
des chaussures	
des sandales	

2 Discover what people are wearing by using the code-breaking key to decipher the sentences below.

e = ♠   u = ♥   o = ♣   s = ♦   t = ✿

J♣ p♣r✿♠ ♥n♠ v♠♦✿♠ ♠✿ ♥n j♠an.

....

♠v♠ p♣r✿♠ ♥n♠ j♥p♠ ♠✿ ♥n ch♠mi♦i♠r.

....

✿♣m p♣r✿♠ ♥n ♦h♣r✿ ♠✿ ♥n ✿♠♠-♦hir✿.

....

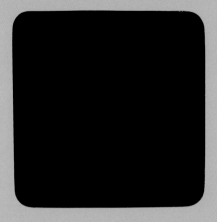

Time filler:
Draw a picture of your favourite outfit. Label the items of clothing in French. Add in details about colours and patterns to extend your list. If you have time, draw outfits for different occasions, such as a birthday party, a day at the beach, and so on.

(3) In each box, draw a picture of the garment described in French.

une écharpe rouge à pois	une robe rose à carreaux	un tee-shirt blanc à rayures vertes	une jupe bleue à fleurs

(4) Finish these sentences. Note the use of the past tense (**j'ai porté**/I wore) and the near future tense (**je vais porter**/I am going to wear).

Aujourd'hui, je porte ....

Hier, j'ai porté ....

Demain, je vais porter ....

(5) Complete these sentences by describing what outfit you will wear.

Pour aller en ville, je vais porter ....

Pour aller à la plage, je vais porter ....

Quel temps fait-il?

Remember that when talking about the weather in French, you often use the verb **faire** (to make). For example, **il fait beau** means "the weather is good" and **il fait froid** means "it is cold".

---

1 Fill in the missing letters in the French descriptions of the weather symbols. **Note:** You may use a dictionary to help you.

  Il pl_____.

 Il f____t nu__g__x.

  Il ne_____.

  I__ __ a des orages.

  Il f__t ch__d.

  Il __it du v_____.

  Il fa____ f_____d.

  Il __it du so____ __ l.

---

2 Describe the weather during the different seasons of the year by filling in the gaps in these sentences. The first one has been done for you.

En hiver, _____il neige_____ et _____il fait froid_____ .

Au printemps, _____ et _____ .

En été, _____ et _____ .

En automne, _____ et _____ .

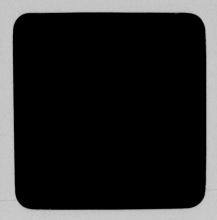

Time filler:
Try this variation of noughts-and-crosses.
Create a noughts-and-crosses grid, with a
different weather symbol (see question 1 below)
drawn in each box. Then before you put a
nought or a cross in a box, you must first say
what the symbol in that box stands for in French!

(3) Complete these sentences, writing what you would wear for the
weather described.

Quand il fait chaud, je porte ....

Quand il fait froid, je porte ....

Quand il pleut, je porte ....

(4) Look at the weather symbols on the map. Then complete the sentences
given below the map. The first one has been done for you.

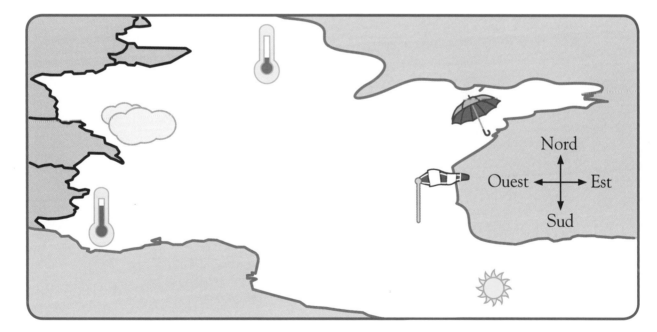

Dans le nord, ___il fait froid___ .

Dans l'ouest, ...

Dans le sud, ...

Dans le nord-est, ...

Dans l'est, ...

Dans le sud-ouest, ...

A l'école

What do you think of the subjects taught in your school? Which ones do you like best? Which ones do you dislike or find difficult? Practise explaining why you think what you think using **parce que...** (because...).

(1) Fill in the gaps on the chart below, showing some of the subjects taught in school. **Note:** You may use a dictionary to help you.

French	English
	maths
	drama
	science
	French
le dessin	
le sport	

French	English
la religion	
la technologie	
	history
	geography
	music
l'informatique	

(2) Translate these English sentences into French.

Sport is okay, but I hate maths.

....

I also like geography, because it's interesting.

....

Drawing is my favourite subject and sport is great, too!

....

I like history, but drama is awful!

....

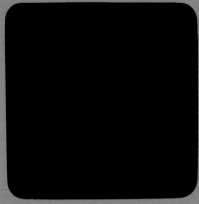

Time filler:
Create a timetable for your ideal week at school. Which subjects would you study? Which ones would you skip? Remember to use the French words for days of the week on your timetable.

(3) Say which school subjects you like and which you dislike by filling in the gaps in these sentences. **Note**: In French, any subject you mention must always have **le, la, l'** or **les** in front of it.

J'aime .... parce que c'est ....

Je n'aime pas .... parce que c'est ....

J'aime beaucoup .... parce que c'est ....

Je détèste .... parce que c'est ....

(4) Translate these French expressions into English.

C'est formidable! ....

C'est intéressant. ....

C'est amusant. ....

C'est super! ....

C'est facile. ....

C'est ok. ....

C'est nul! ....

C'est moche. ....

C'est difficile. ....

La musique

Do you play a musical instrument? Or do you like to sing? Get ready to talk about music on these pages.

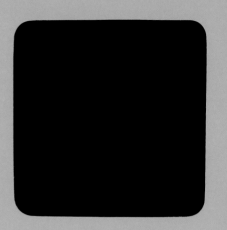

(1) Add the French translations of the English words to this chart, saying whether they are masculine or feminine nouns.

English	French	Masculine or Feminine
clarinet		
saxophone		
piano		
guitar		
trumpet		
drums		
violin		
cello		

(2) Translate these sentences into English.

J'aime la musique classique. ....

J'aime beaucoup la musique pop. ....

J'adore la musique folklorique! ....

J'aime aussi la musique de ballet. ....

Je n'aime pas le rock! ....

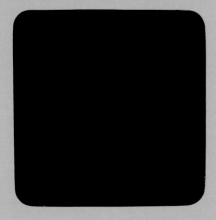

Time filler:
Find a picture of an orchestra in a magazine or book, or on the internet. Can you name all of the instruments in French? Use the chart you have filled in on page 52 and a dictionary to help you.

(3) Translate these sentences into French. **Note:** To say that you play a musical instrument, you use the verb **jouer** (to play) + **de** + the name of the instrument. The first one has been done for you.

I play the saxophone.   Je joue du saxophone.

She plays the clarinet.   ....

Do you play the piano?   ....

He plays the violin.   ....

We play the trumpet.   ....

They play the drums.   ....

They play the guitar.   ....

(4) Translate what these people are saying into English.

Je ne joue pas d'instrument, mais j'aime les concerts.

....

Je ne joue pas d'instrument, mais j'adore chanter.

....

Je joue du violon dans un orchestre et je chante dans un chorale aussi.

....

54

Les nombres 70–1000

Once you pass 70, the French number system is quite different from the English one. It involves some maths. Get ready to work out some higher numbers!

(1) Write the French for these numbers. The maths given after each number should give you a clue.

70 (60 + 10) ....

80 (4 x 20) ....

90 (4 x 20 + 10) ....

(2) Write the French for these numbers. Remember that the French for 100 is **cent** and that you add an "s" to make it plural, as in **six cents** (600).

200 ....   900 ....

300 ....   700 ....

500 ....   800 ....

(3) Reorder the numbers given below, starting with the smallest at the top.

vingt-huit ....

soixante-trois ....

quatre-vingt-dix-sept ....

soixante-treize ....

mille ....

quatre-vingt-six ....

trente-deux ....

quarante et un ....

cent ....

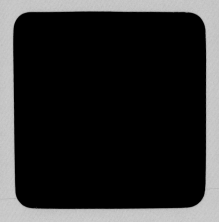

Time filler:
Find the website of a French department store on the internet. Look at the prices given in euros. Then try saying and writing out those prices in French.

(4) Draw lines to match the numbers on the left with the number words on the right.

190   cent trente-quatre

172   cent quatre-vingt-trois

165   cent quatre-vingt-dix

183   cent soixante-douze

134   cent soixante-cinq

(5) Solve these sums. Give your answers first in digits and then in French.

trente et un + quarante   = ...

trente + cinquante-deux   = ...

quatre-vingt-dix + onze   = ...

(6) Write the French for each amount of money.

€ 30.80   ....

€ 200.78   ....

€ 86.43   ....

€ 282.17   ....

€ 120.00   ....

(7) Write the year given below in French.

1971   ....

La nourriture et les boissons

Use **manger** (to eat) and **boire** (to drink) to talk about eating and drinking in French. Make sure you know the different forms of both these verbs before you begin.

(1) Fill in the French words on the chart. Remember to put **le**, **la**, **l'** or **les** before each one. **Note:** You may use a dictionary to help you.

English	French
rice	
meat	
pasta	
bread	
fruit	
cheese	
eggs	
butter	
fish	
soup	
vegetables	
potatoes	
cake	
ice-cream	

(2) Unscramble the French sentences below. Then translate them into English.

du fromage? Veux-tu ....

-tu Veux pain? du ....

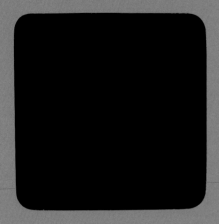

Time filler:
Keep a food diary in French for a day, or even a week. Use the past tense, beginning your sentences with **J'ai mangé...** (I ate...) and **J'ai bu...** (I drank...).

3 Unscramble these French words to reveal a list of drinks.

el tail .... l'aue ....

le afcé .... el sju d'enroga ....

le caoc .... el téh ....

el toochlac .... al melanodi ....

4 Complete these sentences, using the correct French translation of the English word given in brackets.

Vous avez ....? (rice) Je vais prendre .... (cereals)

Vous avez ....? (oil) Je vais prendre .... (jam)

5 Fill in the gaps in these sentences to describe what you usually eat in a day.

Pour mon petit déjeuner, je mange ....
.... Je bois ....

Pour mon déjeuner, je mange ....
.... Je bois ....

Pour mon dîner, je mange ....
.... Je bois ....

Au café

Knowing how to order your favourite snacks
and ice-cream flavours in French is a skill
that could prove to be useful!

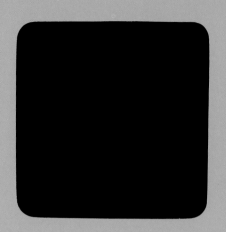

1 Look at the French words for various popular snacks and drinks
in the box below. Then find them in the word-search puzzle.

paquet de chips	orangina	tranche de pizza	coca
glace	portion de frites	hot-dog	hamburger
chocolat chaud	pain	sandwich au fromage	milkshake

s	z	t	r	a	n	c	h	e	d	e	p	i	z	z	a	h
a	d	a	s	d	f	g	h	j	k	l	a	w	f	r	y	p
n	v	c	u	a	i	o	q	p	h	j	q	z	p	w	m	o
d	b	d	h	o	t	-	d	o	g	v	u	x	p	d	l	r
w	n	e	k	x	u	p	e	o	f	c	e	c	a	c	p	t
i	m	t	y	s	y	k	w	u	y	r	t	v	i	v	o	i
c	d	g	h	r	t	l	y	i	q	w	d	b	n	f	i	o
h	a	m	b	u	r	g	e	r	b	m	e	r	k	r	i	n
a	e	i	a	s	f	g	h	j	k	l	c	t	g	t	y	d
u	t	l	z	c	v	x	b	n	m	l	h	y	o	g	u	e
f	y	k	c	o	g	l	a	c	e	m	i	u	r	b	j	f
r	u	s	v	i	q	r	f	o	v	b	p	i	a	n	m	r
o	i	h	d	u	a	d	h	c	d	a	s	o	n	y	t	i
m	o	a	e	h	z	e	o	a	u	i	j	k	g	w	r	t
a	p	k	z	x	c	v	b	g	t	c	v	b	i	n	m	e
g	y	e	q	w	e	r	t	y	u	i	i	o	n	p	k	s
e	r	i	c	h	o	c	o	l	a	t	c	h	a	u	d	c

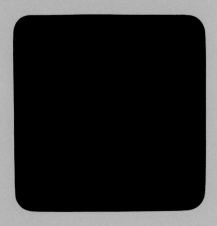

Time filler:
France is famous for its delicious cakes and breads. How many different kinds can you name? Try to write as long a list as you can. Use the internet to help you.

2 Translate these sentences into English.

Le menu, s'il vous plaît? ....

Vous avez choisi? ....

Vous désirez? ....

L'addition, s'il vous plaît? ....

3 Unscramble these food orders.

une s'il frites, Je plaît. vous portion de voudrais

....

fromage, Je plaît. s'il sandwich voudrais au un vous

....

voudrais Je de tranche une s'il pizza, vous plaît.

....

milkshake, vous plaît. un Je s'il voudrais

....

4 Draw lines to match these ice-cream flavours with their English translations.

une glace au chocolat   a strawberry ice-cream

une glace au cassis   a vanilla ice-cream

une glace à la fraise   a blackcurrant ice-cream

une glace à la vanille   a chocolate ice-cream

Le corps

When learning the French words for parts of the body, look out for one or two irregular plurals. Can you spot them?

1 Fill in the missing letters in these French words for parts of the body.
Note: You may use a dictionary to help you.

les br__s   le d__s   les orei__les   la go__ge

les ma__ns   le co__   la bou__he   les épa__les

les ye__x   la tê__e   les jam__es   les ge__oux

2 Look at the monkey. Add numbers to the list next to it to say how many of each body part the monkey has.

.... oreilles   .... dos

.... yeux   .... bouche

.... mains   .... pieds

.... jambes   .... nez

.... bras   .... tête

.... ventre   .... queue

3 J'ai mal à… can be translated as "I have a pain in…". Choose the right preposition (**au**, **à la**, **à l'**, **aux**) to complete these sentences about bodily aches and pains.

J'ai mal .... dents.   J'ai mal .... ventre.

J'ai mal .... yeux.   J'ai mal .... tête.

J'ai mal .... oreille.   J'ai mal .... dos.

Time filler:
Create your own monster! Draw a picture of it and colour it in. Now describe your monster in French. How many heads does it have? How many arms? How many eyes and how many legs? What colour is it?

(4) Find the French word for each English clue to complete the crossword puzzle below.

Across

1. stomach ....
2. fingers ....
3. nose ....
4. ears ....
5. eyes ....

Down

1. mouth ....
2. hands ....
3. body ....
4. knees ....
5. feet ....
6. teeth ....
7. legs ....

Les vacances

Try using the past tense to talk about what you did on holiday. Just as in English, in French there are different types of past tense. Make sure you know when you use **le passé composé** (the perfect tense) and when you use **l'imparfait** (the imperfect tense).

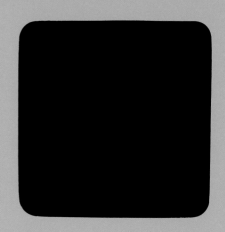

1 Translate these sentences into French. **Note:** You need to use the correct form of **avoir** + **voyagé** to write your answers.

I travelled by plane. ....

He travelled by car. ....

We travelled by boat. ....

2 Translate these sentences into French. **Note:** You need to use the correct form of **être** + **allé(e)(s)** to write your answers.

Pierre went to Italy. ....

Sophie went to France. ....

My sisters went to Africa. ....

My parents went to Portugal. ....

3 Choose the correct form of **avoir** or **être** to complete these sentences.

Nous .... allés à une église.

Il ..... visité des monuments.

Elles .... allées à la plage.

Tu ..... fait de la rando?

J' ..... acheté des souvenirs.

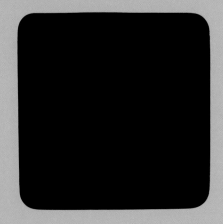

Time filler:
Getting ready to go on a holiday is always fun. What do you need to buy before you go? Make a list in French to take with you when you go shopping. Start it with **Je vais acheter...** (I am going to buy...).

4 Here are some useful French expressions to help you say what you thought about some of the things you did on holiday. Draw lines to match them to their English translations.

C'était marrant.   It was dull.

C'était barbant.   It was frightening.

C'était rapide.   It was great!

C'était passionnant!   It was funny.

C'était terrifiant.   It was fast.

C'était chouette!   It was exciting!

5 You may have visited an amusement park while on holiday. Choose the correct form of **avoir** + **vu** to complete these sentences and say what your family saw on the ghost-train ride. Then write the English translation.

Ma sœur .... un loup-garou.

....

Mon frère .... un vampire.

....

Mes parents .... des araignées.

....

J' .... un squelette.

....

Beat the clock 3

Write the correct present tense form of the verbs shown in brackets below. Remember that they are all regular verbs that end in **-re**. **Vas-y!**

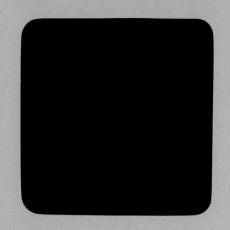

Je (decendre) ....

Tu (perdre) ....

Il (vendre) ....

Nous (decendre) ....

Ils (perdre) ....

Elle (attendre) ....

J' (entendre) ....

Nous (entendre) ....

Je (rendre) ....

Il (répondre) ....

Tu (étendre) ....

Elle (perdre) ....

Nous (pendre) ....

Elles (attendre) ....

Elle (vendre) ....

Il (attendre) ....

Tu (decendre) ....

Je (perdre) ....

Ils (vendre) ....

Ils (attendre) ....

Tu (entendre) ....

Vous (decendre) ....

Tu (rendre) ....

Il (étendre) ....

Tu (pendre) ....

Je (répondre) ....

Vous (entendre) ....

Je (vendre) ....

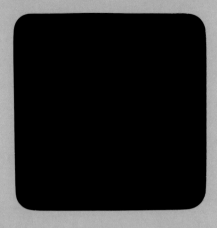

Time filler:
Translate each infinitive verb in the list below into English. Keep testing yourself on these verbs – their meaning and present tense. They are used frequently in French and you will need to be familiar with them.

Il (decendre) ....

Nous (perdre) ....

Tu (vendre) ....

Vous (attendre) ....

Il (entendre) ....

Il (rendre) ....

Elle (étendre) ....

Elles (decendre) ....

Nous (attendre) ....

Tu (répondre) ....

Il (pendre) ....

Ils (entendre) ....

Elles (perdre) ....

Nous (vendre) ....

J' (attendre) ....

Il (perdre) ....

Elle (entendre) ....

Elle (descendre) ....

Vous (vendre) ....

Elles (entendre) ....

Tu (attendre) ....

Ils (decendre) ....

Vous (perdre) ....

Elle (rendre) ....

Nous (étendre) ....

Il (répondre) ....

Vous (pendre) ....

Elles (vendre) ....

Answers:

04–05 Bonjour! Ça va?
06–07 Les nombres 1–20

4

1. **Bonjour** means "hello" and the more informal **salut** can be translated as "hi". Write the best greeting for each of these people.

your friend ___salut___	a policeman ___bonjour___
your teacher ___bonjour___	your mother ___salut___

2. Here are three French expressions that you might use to say how you feel. Draw lines to match each one to a picture below.

Ça ne va pas.   Ça va comme ci, comme ça.   Ça va bien, merci.

3. To be polite, use **monsieur** (sir), **madame** (madam) and **mademoiselle** (miss) with your greetings. Say **au revoir** (goodbye) politely to the people in these pictures.

Au revoir, mademoiselle!   Au revoir, monsieur!   Au revoir, madame!

5

4. Here are two ways of asking "What is your name?" in French, but the vowels are missing. Add the vowels to complete each sentence.

Comment tu t'appelles?

Comment t'appelles-tu?

5. Match each French name with its English equivalent.

Stéphanie   Éléonore   Étienne   Édouard   Pierre

Stephen   Stephanie   Peter   Eleanor   Edward

6. Translate each phrase from English to French. Use the French equivalent of people's names.

Goodbye, Stephen!	Au revoir, Étienne!
My name is Edward.	Je m'appelle Édouard.
How are you, Peter?	Ça va, Pierre?

7. The words in these greetings are all mixed up. Unscramble them and write each sentence correctly.

Ça va merci. bien,	Ça va bien, merci.
t'appelles-tu? Comment	Comment t'appelles-tu?
madame! Bonjour,	Bonjour, madame!

The activities on these pages give practice in making basic introductions in French. Make sure that as well as giving answers, your child practises asking simple questions. When asking a question, encourage your child to raise his or her voice at the end. Ensure that he or she uses the polite form **Bonjour** and **Monsieur, Madame** or **Mademoiselle**, to say hello to people in more formal situations.

6

1. A rocket is about to be launched. Below is the countdown in French, but some of the numbers are missing. Fill in the gaps.

dix, neuf, ___huit___, **sept**, ___six___, **cinq**, quatre, ___trois___, ___deux___, ___un___, zéro! Feu!

2. Write the number for each French number word.

un ___1___	deux ___2___	quatre ___4___
sept ___7___	huit ___8___	dix ___10___
onze ___11___	douze ___12___	treize ___13___
quinze ___15___	dix-sept ___17___	vingt ___20___

3. Complete each calculation in French.

dix + sept = ___dix-sept___	huit + deux = ___dix___
cinq + sept = ___douze___	douze – un = ___onze___
trois x deux = ___six___	vingt – cinq = ___quinze___

4. Circle the words that have silent last letters.

un   (deux)   (trois)   cinq   sept

7

5. Translate each number into French. Then complete the crossword.

Across
1. two ___deux___
2. eight ___huit___
3. nine ___neuf___
4. thirteen ___treize___
5. twenty ___vingt___

Down
1. eleven ___onze___
2. twelve ___douze___
3. three ___trois___
4. ten ___dix___
5. seven ___sept___

It is a good idea to keep revisiting numbers. Children may find it helpful to try saying numbers in French whenever they notice them around the house, or when they are out and about. Your child can also try using French numbers in games with simple scores or games involving dice.

Answers:

08–09 Ma famille
10–11 Quel âge as-tu?

8

1 Read the information given in the chart below. Then use it to write the name of the child shown in each picture.

Je m'appelle Thomas. J'ai une sœur et un frère.	Je m'appelle Sophie. J'ai deux frères.
Je m'appelle Juliette. J'ai une sœur. Je n'ai pas de frère.	Je m'appelle Frédéric. Je n'ai ni frères ni sœurs.

Frédéric

Juliette

Sophie

Thomas

2 Translate these phrases. Remember to use the correct French word for "my" (**mon, ma** or **mes**) in each case.

my brother ___mon frère___   my mother ___ma mère___
my grandmother ___ma grand-mère___   my sisters ___mes sœurs___

9

3 Look at the people in this family. Then complete each sentence.

Christelle · André · Agnès · Jean-Pierre
Jean · Louis
David · Sylvie

Le père s'appelle ___Jean-Pierre___ . La mère s'appelle ___Christelle___ .
Le grand-père s'appelle ___André___ . La grand-mère s'appelle ___Agnès___ .
Le petit garcon s'appelle ___David___ . La sœur s'appelle ___Sylvie___ .
Les bébés s'appellent ___Louis et Jean___ .
Les enfants s'appellent ___David, Sylvie, Louis et Jean___ .

4 Circle the correct form of the verb **s'appeler** in each sentence.

Mes frères s'appelle / (s'appellent) Adrien et Charles.

La sœur de David (s'appelle) / s'appellent Élisabeth.

Mes parents s'appelle / (s'appellent) Louis et Marie.

By working through this page, your child will be motivated to write about their family and friends. Children will enjoy using authentic French names, which they can find on the internet. Point out the different verb endings for **s'appeler**. Ask how the spelling changes when talking about one person or more than one person – we need to add **e** or **ent**, respectively.

10

1 Look at each picture. Then complete each sentence by writing the missing word.

J'ai ___sept___ ans.
J'ai ___neuf___ ans.
J'ai ___seize___ ans.
J'ai ___trois___ ans.
J'ai ___onze___ ans.

11

2 Here is a sheet from a notebook, showing the names and ages of some children taken on a school trip. Next to it, write sentences in French, stating each child's age. The first one has been done for you.

Prénom	Age
Pierre	7
Édouard	11
Mustafa	9
Stéphanie	8
Luc	10
Christelle	12

Pierre a sept ans.
Édouard a onze ans.
Mustafa a neuf ans.
Stéphanie a huit ans.
Luc a dix ans.
Christelle a douze ans.

3 Fill in the missing letters to complete each sentence.

Ma sœur a qua_t_re ans.   J'a_i_ s_e_pt an_s_.
M_o_n frè_r_e a n_eu_f ans.   J'ai o_n_ze ans.

4 Translate these sentences into French.

He is ten. ___Il a dix ans.___
She is eight years old. ___Elle a huit ans.___
He is fourteen. ___Il a quatorze ans.___
She is three. ___Elle a trois ans.___

Your child needs to practise the question form – **Quel âge as-tu?** – as well as ways to reply. Point out the use of accents. Show your child the circumflex on **âge**, the acute accent on **Édouard** and the grave accent on **frère**.

It is helpful for your child to be aware from the start that accents can change sounds and are an important part of the correct spelling of a word.

Answers:

12–13 Dans mon cartable
14–15 Les nombres 20–69

12

1 Fill in the chart. Add the French word for each object listed in English, as well as the correct French word for "the" (**le**, **la** or **les**) that you would use in each case. **Note:** You may use a dictionary to help you.

English	le, la or les	French
pencil	le	crayon
pen	le	stylo
rubber	la	gomme
pencil case	la	trousse
calculator	la	calculatrice
felt-tip pen	le	feutre
pencil sharpener	le	taille-crayon
school bag	le	cartable
notebook	le	cahier
ruler	la	règle

2 Circle the correct French word for "a/an" in each phrase.

(un)/ une sac   un /(une)règle
un /(une)gomme   (un)/ une crayon
(un)/ une stylo   un /(une)trousse
(un)/ une feutre   un /(une)calculatrice
(un)/ une cahier   (un)/ une taille-crayon

13

3 The following sentence is written as a code.

11 4 1 23   18 15 1   26 4 6 9 4 17 2 7,   20' 4 14 25 1   23 9 13 2 15.

Use this code-breaking chart to reveal what letter each number in the coded sentence stands for. Then write the decoded message.

a	b	c	d	e	i	j	l	m	n	o	r	s	t	u	y
4	17	26	11	7	14	20	2	18	1	15	6	23	9	25	13

Dans mon cartable, j'ai un stylo.

4 Find the French words for ten classroom objects in this word-search puzzle.
Hint: All the words can be found on the chart on page 12.

s	p	u	f	x	f	t	r	o	u	s	s	e
t	a	l	l	l	e	-	c	r	a	y	o	n
y	z	f	c	m	u	h	f	è	i	p	h	a
l	e	r	x	n	t	i	r	g	t	j	p	g
o	b	q	z	s	r	c	d	l	w	c	r	o
e	i	w	p	l	e	l	g	e	s	a	e	m
l	o	u	c	r	a	y	o	n	v	h	t	m
l	c	a	l	c	u	l	a	t	r	i	c	e
b	u	f	p	a	i	i	g	o	z	e	a	h
c	a	r	t	a	b	l	e	a	t	r	b	c

These pages provide a good opportunity to talk about the gender of nouns. Explain that the French words for "a/ an" and "the" will change depending on whether they are followed by a masculine, feminine or plural noun.

14

1 Complete each number word in the chart.

Number	Number word
23	vingt- trois
34	trente -quatre
41	quarante et un
52	cinquante -deux
69	soixante- neuf

2 Write these numbers as digits.

trente et un [31]   soixante-sept [67]   vingt-quatre [24]

vingt-six [26]   cinquante-huit [58]   quarante-neuf [49]

3 Write the French for each number.

51 cinquante et un   42 quarante-deux   63 soixante-trois

29 vingt-neuf   35 trente-cinq   57 cinquante-sept

4 Write the next two numbers in each sequence.

vingt et un, vingt-deux,   vingt-trois, vingt-quatre

quarante-six, quarante-sept,   quarante-huit, quarante-neuf

15

5 Solve these sums. Write the answers, first in digits and then in French.

3 x 7 = [21] vingt et un   6 x 7 = [42] quarante-deux
9 x 3 = [27] vingt-sept   12 x 3 = [36] trente-six
6 x 8 = [48] quarante-huit   10 x 5 = [50] cinquante
8 x 8 = [64] soixante-quatre   11 x 5 = [55] cinquante-cinq
7 x 9 = [63] soixante-trois   11 x 3 = [33] trente-trois

6 In this word-search puzzle, find the French words for the ten numbers that are answers to the sums in question 5.

c	i	n	q	u	a	n	t	e	-	c	i	n	q	f	t
e	r	t	u	i	p	w	r	p	f	y	q	u	t	w	r
q	u	a	r	a	n	t	e	-	h	u	i	t	r	e	e
r	t	y	u	p	v	i	n	g	t	-	s	e	p	t	n
s	q	u	a	r	a	n	t	e	-	d	e	u	x	p	t
s	o	i	x	a	n	t	e	-	q	u	a	t	r	e	e
t	u	v	i	n	x	t	-	e	t	l	u	n	e	f	-
c	i	n	t	e	v	i	s	e	p	h	u	t	r	e	t
i	m	i	e	g	h	c	i	n	q	u	a	n	t	e	r
n	a	h	t	r	u	i	x	p	l	e	a	h	u	i	o
s	o	i	x	a	n	t	e	-	t	r	o	i	s	t	i
q	u	a	v	i	n	g	t	e	t	u	n	u	x	w	s

For numbers such as 21 and 31, children will need a reminder to include **et**, which helps with pronunciation. For example, the French for 21 is **vingt et un**. Numbers need lots of reinforcement. Your child may enjoy counting games in French. For example, try clapping a number of times, then ask your child to tell you in French how many times you've clapped.

Answers:

16–17 Les mois
18–19 Les adjectifs
20–21 Beat the clock 1, see p.80

16

① Select French words for the months of the year from the chart below to match the list of months in English.

août	janvier	septembre	mars	novembre	avril
février	mai	juin	octobre	décembre	juillet

January _____janvier_____

February _____février_____

March _____mars_____

April _____avril_____

May _____mai_____

June _____juin_____

July _____juillet_____

August _____août_____

September _____septembre_____

October _____octobre_____

November _____novembre_____

December _____décembre_____

② Use the first letter and the number of spaces provided as clues to work out the birthday month of each child.

Mon anniversaire est le 26 j u i n .

Mon anniversaire est le 17 a v r i l .

Mon anniversaire est le 10 f é v r i e r .

Mon anniversaire est le 31 a o û t .

17

③ Quelle est la date de ton anniversaire?
When is your birthday? Answers may vary.

....

④ The letters have fallen out of the bottom of this puzzle grid! On the way down, they got mixed up, although they are still in their correct rows. Unscramble them to discover the mystery birthday date.

		m	o	n					
a	n	n	i	v	e	r	s	a	i	r	e
		e	s	t		l	e		
v	i	n	g	t		e	t		u	n
s	e	p	t	e	m	b	r	e	

o n m
e a i r s v e r n i n a
s t l e e
u n t g i n e t v
m e e t b p r s e

⑤ Continue this sequence.

mars   avril   mai   _____juin_____   _____juillet_____   _____août_____

It is a good idea to start by asking children what month their birthday is in and then progress to combining numbers and months. Your child may enjoy keeping a small birthday book in French, where he or she records the birthdays of family and friends. Keep reminding your child that in French, months begin with a lowercase letter, unlike in English.

18

① Write the feminine form and the English translation for each adjective listed on the chart. **Note:** You may use a dictionary to help you.

French (Masculine)	French (Feminine)	English
gentil	gentille	kind
timide	timide	shy
gourmand	gourmande	greedy
petit	petite	small
grand	grande	big/tall
sportif	sportive	sporty
méchant	méchante	naughty
beau	belle	handsome/beautiful
paresseux	paresseuse	lazy
mignon	mignonne	cute
marrant	marrante	funny
sympa	sympa	nice

② Complete the following sentences using adjectives from the chart above.

Je suis _____Answers may vary._____ et _____Answers may vary._____ .

Ma mère est _____Answers may vary._____ et _____Answers may vary._____ .

19

③ Choose your favourite character from a book or a film. Write a few sentences describing him or her in French. Answers may vary.

....
....
....
....

④ Circle the adjective in each French sentence that correctly matches the English sentences.

He has brown hair. | Il a les cheveux (bruns)/ roux / blonds / noirs.

She has red hair. | Elle a les cheveux bruns /(roux)/ blonds / noirs.

He has green eyes. | Il a les yeux marron / bleus /(verts)/ gris.

She has blue eyes. | Elle a les yeux marron /(bleus)/ verts / gris.

⑤ Write a brief description of yourself in French. Use **Je suis**... (I am...) and **J'ai**... (I have...) to begin your sentences. Answers may vary.

....
....
....
....

Once children know about the gender of nouns, they can begin using adjectives, which need to agree with nouns. Ask your child to tell you how the spelling of masculine and feminine adjectives change. Look for patterns, for example the masculine ending **–if** changes to **–ive** and **–eux** changes to **–euse**. Explain that for a feminine adjective, we often add an **e** at the end.

Answers:

22–23 Les couleurs
24–25 Les jours de la semaine

22

① Translate the English colour words into French.

red — rouge
yellow — jaune
black — noir
grey — gris
orange — orange
blue — bleu
brown — marron
violet — violet
green — vert

② Unscramble these French colour words.

canbl — blanc
georu — rouge
reogan — orange
romran — marron
trev — vert
uneja — jaune

23

③ Fill in the chart by writing the different French forms of each colour given in English.

English	French (Masculine/Plural)	French (Feminine/Plural)
red	rouge/rouges	rouge/rouges
yellow	jaune/jaunes	jaune/jaunes
blue	bleu/bleus	bleue/bleues
green	vert/verts	verte/vertes
brown	marron/marron	marron/marron
orange	orange/orange	orange/orange
white	blanc/blancs	blanche/blanches
black	noir/noirs	noire/noires
grey	gris/gris	grise/grises
violet	violet/violets	violette/violettes
pink	rose/roses	rose/roses

④ Spot the mistakes! Write each phrase using the correct form of the adjective.

une gomme violete — une gomme violette
des crayons marrons — des crayons marron
un chapeau rouges — un chapeau rouge
ma robe blanc — ma robe blanche

Remind your child that colours are adjectives and they need to agree with the noun they describe. This could mean using masculine, feminine, masculine plural or feminine plural. Point out that unlike in English, French colours go after the noun. Your child will need to watch out for invariable adjectives, such as **orange**, where the spelling remains the same.

24

① Draw a line linking each day in French to its English equivalent.

mardi — Tuesday
samedi — Saturday
jeudi — Thursday
lundi — Monday
mercredi — Wednesday
dimanche — Sunday
vendredi — Friday

② Continue each sequence.

mardi — mercredi — jeudi — vendredi
vendredi — samedi — dimanche — lundi
dimanche — lundi — mardi — mercredi
mercredi — jeudi — vendredi — samedi

25

③ Complete these sentences.

Avant mardi, c'est lundi.
Après samedi, c'est dimanche.
Avant vendredi, c'est jeudi.
Après lundi, c'est mardi.

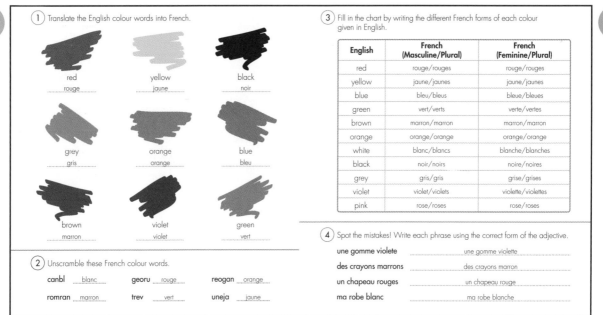

④ Translate the following dates into French.

Monday, 3rd July — lundi 3 juillet
Saturday, 1st September — samedi 1 septembre
Wednesday, 5th January — mercredi 5 janvier

⑤ Answer the questions in French. Answers may vary.

What is the date tomorrow?
What was the date yesterday?
What will the date be in two days time?

Encourage your child to keep a simple diary in French, using a page for each week. Divide each page into seven sections and write the days in French. Your child could draw pictures and use simple French phrases to remind him or her about what is happening each day. He or she should know that we use **le premier** for the first day of a month. For example, we say **samedi le premier septembre** for Saturday, 1st September.

Answers:

26–27 Les animaux
28–29 La maison

26

1 In each pair, circle the smaller animal. Use a dictionary to look up any word that you do not know.

(un chien)	un éléphant
(un chat)	un tigre
un cheval	(une souris)
(un oiseau)	un gorille
un lapin	(une abeille)
(une grenouille)	un mouton

2 Unscramble the sentences below.

chiens. a deux Pierre _____ Pierre a deux chiens.

Sophie trois a chevaux. _____ Sophie a trois chevaux.

a quatre David oiseaux. _____ David a quatre oiseaux.

3 Which animals do you prefer? Answer in full sentences. Answers may vary.

Tu préfères les chats ou les chiens?

.....

Tu préfères les tortues ou les poissons rouges?

.....

27

4 Work out which animal is making the sounds.

miaou — Quel animal fait miaou?
Un chat fait miaou.

Quel animal fait coin-coin? — coin-coin
Un canard fait coin-coin.

cocorico — Quel animal fait cocorico?
Un coq fait cocorico.

Quel animal fait ouah-ouah? — ouah-ouah
Un chien fait ouah-ouah.

5 Read out the list of animals in the box below.

la grenouille	la vache	le mouton	le tigre	le canard	le gorille

Now sort the animals by where you are most likely to see each one.

dans le lac?	à la ferme?	dans le zoo?
la grenouille	la vache	le gorille
le canard	le mouton	le tigre

Talking about animals is a good opportunity for your child to practise the verb **avoir**. For example, **Sophie a trois chevaux**. Refer to pages 10, 13 and 18, where your child also makes use of **j'ai**, **il a** and **elle a**. Also ask him or her what they notice about plural spellings in this section. Can your child identify and point out the irregular plurals **chevaux** and **oiseaux**?

28

1 Translate these words into English. **Note:** You may use a dictionary to help you.

le salon	sitting room	le bureau	study
le grenier	attic	le sous-sol	basement
la cuisine	kitchen	la salle de bains	bathroom
la chambre	bedroom	la salle à manger	dining room
l'escalier	staircase	le jardin	garden
la cave	cellar	la chambre d'enfants	nursery

2 Look at these lists of things you might find in some of the rooms in your house. Circle the object in each list that would be out of place.

La cuisine:
l'évier
(l'oreiller)
le frigo
le four

Le salon:
(l'évier)
le sofa
les rideaux
le fauteuil

La chambre:
le lit
le tapis
l'oreiller
(le four)

La salle de bains:
la douche
le lavabo
(le lit)
la serviette

29

3 Look at the picture. Then answer the questions below in French.

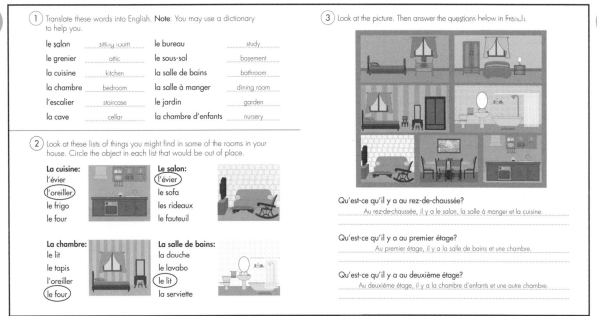

Qu'est-ce qu'il y a au rez-de-chaussée?
Au rez-de-chaussée, il y a le salon, la salle à manger et la cuisine.

Qu'est-ce qu'il y a au premier étage?
Au premier étage, il y a la salle de bains et une chambre.

Qu'est-ce qu'il y a au deuxième étage?
Au deuxième étage, il y a la chambre d'enfants et une autre chambre.

On these pages, your child is encouraged to use a dictionary. Guide your child to use the English-French and French-English sections. Encourage your child to keep a vocabulary book with pages marked with the letters of the alphabet to note down new words he or she has discovered. This activity will help your child to expand his or her French vocabulary gradually.

Answers:

30–31 Où habites-tu?
32–33 Les pays

30

(1) Complete the chart by adding the English translations.

French	English
une maison	a house
un appartement	a flat
une maison jumelée	a semi-detached house
une maison individuelle	a detached house
une maison mitoyenne	a terraced house
un bungalow	a bungalow

(2) Find out what the French expressions mean by unscrambling their English translations.

French	English		
en ville	in tnow	=	in town
à la campagne	in the cidentrouys	=	in the countryside
en banlieue	in the rbssubu	=	in the suburbs
à la montagne	in the itmounasn	=	in the mountains
au bord de la mer	by the esa	=	by the sea

31

(3) Insert the correct form of the present tense of the verb **habiter** (to live) in these sentences.

J' _habite_ à Londres.

Il _habite_ au bord de la mer.

Tu _habites_ en banlieue.

Ils _habitent_ à la campagne.

Nous _habitons_ en ville.

Vous _habitez_ dans un village.

(4) Translate these French sentences into English.

J'habite avec mes parents dans une maison jumelée.
I live with my parents in a semi-detached house.

Elle habite avec sa mère dans un grand appartement.
She lives with her mother in a big flat.

(5) Translate these English sentences into French.

My grandparents live on an old farm in the mountains.
Mes grandparents habitent dans une vieille ferme à la montagne.

My cousins live in a bungalow by the sea.
Mes cousins habitent dans un bungalow au bord de la mer.

The forms French verbs take are very different from English verbs. This section provides a good opportunity to practise the different endings of an **–er** verb (**habiter**). Ask your child which letters need to be added to **habit–** for each pronoun (**je**, **tu**, **il**, **elle**, **nous**, **vous**, **ils**, **elles**).

32

(1) Translate these sentences from English to French. **Note:** You may use a dictionary to help you.

I live in France.
J'habite en France.

I live by the sea in Greece.
J'habite au bord de la mer en Grèce.

I work in the Netherlands.
Je travaille aux Pays-Bas.

He lives in the mountains in Italy.
Il habite à la montagne en Italie.

She lives in Canada.
Elle habite au Canada.

He is going to Wales.
Il va au Pays de Galles.

I am going to the USA.
Je vais aux États-Unis.

She lives in Spain.
Elle habite en Espagne.

They live in the countryside in Portugal.
Ils habitent à la campagne au Portugal.

33

(2) Fill in the chart by writing the French name for each country. **Note:** You may use a dictionary to help you.

English	French
Scotland	L'Écosse
England	L'Angleterre
Ireland	L'Irlande
Belgium	La Belgique
Germany	L'Allemagne
Denmark	Le Danemark
Switzerland	La Suisse
Turkey	La Turquie
Norway	La Norvège

(3) Translate the sentences below from English to French.

I work in London. _Je travaille à Londres._
I am going to Barcelona. _Je vais à Barcelone._
I live in Paris. _J'habite à Paris._

(4) Write the correct French translation for "in" or "to" that you would use before each of these destinations.

_à_ New York _en_ Californie _aux_ États-Unis

In this activity, your child will gain practice in using some forms of the irregular verb **aller** – **je vais** and **il/elle va**. For further practice, children may enjoy building sentences of their own, modelled on the sentences used here. Encourage your child to combine **je vais/il va/elle va** with different cities and countries.

Answers:

34–35 En ville
36–37 Où est…?

34

1 Complete the chart by adding the English translations.
Note: You may use a dictionary to help you.

French	English
le supermarché	the supermarket
la poste	the post office
l'école	the school
la banque	the bank
le parc	the park
le musée	the museum
la librairie	the bookshop
le café	the café
l'hôpital	the hospital
la gare	the station
la piscine	the swimming pool
le restaurant	the restaurant

2 Answer these questions in French.

Où est-ce qu'on achète de la viande? ..... la boucherie

Où est-ce qu'on achète des gâteaux? ..... la pâtisserie

Où est-ce qu'on achète du pain? ..... la boulangerie

35

3 Complete this chart by adding the correct form of the present tense of the verb **aller** (to go).

English	French
I go	Je vais
You (singular) go	Tu vas
He/she goes	Il/Elle va
We go	Nous allons
You (plural) go	Vous allez
They go	Il/Elles vont

4 Choose the right way to say "to" – **au**, **à la**, **à l'** or **aux** – to complete the phrases below.

Je vais à l' hôtel. | Ils vont au cinéma.

Tu vas au collège. | Nous allons à la station-service.

5 Use the right form of the verb **aller** (to go) and the right way of saying "to" to complete the sentences below.

Sophie va à l' église. | Je vais au restaurant.

Nous allons aux magasins. | Tu vas à la banque?

Il va à l' hôpital. | Elles vont à la coiffeuse.

Ils vont au stade. | Mon père va au musée.

These pages will help your child grasp the use of the verb **aller**. He or she will also begin to use the preposition **à**, which becomes **au**, **à la** or **aux** depending on whether the noun that follows it is masculine, feminine or plural. **À l'** is used for a noun starting with a vowel or a silent "h".

36

1 Unscramble these sentences to reveal three requests for directions.

je Comment aller peux à gare? la
..... Comment je peux aller à la gare?

Madame, Pardon aller poste? à la pour
..... Pardon Madame, pour aller à la poste?

Pardon Monsieur, le où est restaurant?
..... Pardon Monsieur, où est le restaurant?

2 Draw lines linking the French phrases with their English translations.

en face de — between
près de — opposite
à côté de — near
devant — in front of
entre — behind
derrière — next to

3 Choose from **du**, **de la**, **de l'** or **des** to complete the directions below.

Il y a une poste en face ..... de la ..... gare.

Il y a une banque près ..... de l' ..... hôtel.

Il y a un office de tourisme près ..... des ..... magasins.

37

4 Translate these English sentences into French.

The bank is between the church and the museum.
..... La banque est entre l'église et le musée.

My school is near my house and the park.
..... Mon école est près de ma maison et du parc.

The bookshop is next to the café and the station.
..... La librairie est à côté du café et de la gare.

5 Look at these symbols for various directions.

↑ Allez tout droit   → Tournez à droite   ← Tournez à gauche

⌐ Prenez la deuxième rue à droite   ⌐ Prenez la première rue à gauche

Now write in French what the sequences of symbols below mean:

↑ ⌐ ..... Allez tout droit et prenez la deuxième rue à droite.

⌐ → ..... Prenez la première rue à gauche et tournez à droite.

↑ ← ..... Allez tout droit et tournez à gauche.

In this section, your child will practise three different model sentences to ask for directions. He or she will also need to choose the correct form – **du**, **de la** or **des** – to complete directions, depending on whether the noun that follows is masculine, feminine or plural. Remind your child to use **de l'** in front of a vowel or a silent "h".

74

Answers:

38–39 Le temps libre
40–41 Quelle heure est-il?
42–43 Beat the clock 2, see p.80

38

① Fill in the chart by ticking (✔) the correct column to say which of the sports listed is masculine or feminine, and adding the English translation.
Note: You may use a dictionary to help you.

French	Masculine	Feminine	English
tennis	✔		tennis
foot	✔		football
équitation		✔	horseriding
natation		✔	swimming
gymnastique		✔	gymnastics
vélo	✔		cycling
planche à voile		✔	windsurfing

② Use the correct form of **faire de** to complete the sentences below.
Remember: de changes to **du**, **de la** or **de l'**, depending on whether the French word for the activity following it is masculine or feminine.

Je _fais_ _du_ ski.

Nous _faisons_ _de l'_ équitation.

Tu _fais_ _de la_ natation.

Il _fait_ _de la_ gymnastique.

39

③ Write the correct form of **jouer à** or **faire de** to complete each sentence.

Elles _font_ _du_ skate.

Tu _joues_ _au_ tennis.

Nous _jouons_ _au_ foot.

Je _fais_ _de la_ natation.

Il _fait_ _de la_ gymnastique.

Vous _faites_ _de l'_ équitation.

④ Write about which sports you like and which you dislike by completing the following sentences. Answers may vary.

J'aime _____.

Je n'aime pas _____.

J'adore _____.

Je détèste _____.

Mon sport préféré, c'est _____.

⑤ Choose the correct verb from the box below to complete the sentences.

écouter	aller	faire	lire

J'aime _aller_ au cinéma.

J'aime _lire_ des livres.

J'aime _faire_ les magasins.

J'aime _écouter_ de la musique.

Here your child will gain further practice in selecting **du**, **de la** or **de l'** correctly. He or she will also practise the useful model phrase **J'aime** + an infinitive verb. Encourage children to build further sentences of their own using this model, saying they enjoy doing a variety of activities.

40

① Draw lines to match the time on each clock with the correct sentence.

Il est six heures.   Il est neuf heures.   Il est trois heures.

② Add **et quart**, **et demie** or **moins le quart** to complete the French translations on the chart below.

English	French
It is quarter past two.	Il est deux heures _et quart_.
It is quarter past one.	Il est une heure _et quart_.
It is half past five.	Il est cinq heures _et demie_.
It is half past four.	Il est quatre heures _et demie_.
It is quarter to ten.	Il est dix heures _moins le quart_.
It is quarter to eleven.	Il est onze heures _moins le quart_.

③ Unscramble these English sentences. Then translate them into French.

I'ts madyid.   _It's midday_ .   Il est midi .

Its' nhtigmdi.   _It's midnight_ .   Il est minuit .

41

④ Circle the correct sentence to match the time on each clock.

Il est deux heures.
(Il est une heure dix.)
Il est cinq heures.

(Il est quatre heures moins le quart.)
Il est deux heures moins le quart.
Il est trois heures moins le quart.

⑤ Write the time shown on the digital clocks in French.

18 : 00 — Il est six heures du soir.

14 : 00 — Il est deux heures de l'après-midi.

23 : 00 — Il est onze heures du soir.

⑥ Answer these questions about how you spend your evening. To say at a specific time, use **à** + the time, for example, **à huit heures** (at eight o'clock). Answers may vary.

À quelle heure est-ce que tu fais tes devoirs?

À quelle heure est-ce que tu regardes la télévision?

Before starting these activities, it is a good idea to reinforce the numbers 1 to 12. Your child might struggle to use the correct hour when using **moins le quart**. First, make sure he or she understands which hour the long hand is approaching. Then remind him or her that for any time other than one o'clock, the plural form **heures** will need to be used.

Answers:

44–45 Ma routine
46–47 Les vêtements

44

1 Choose reflexive pronouns from the box below to complete the different forms of the present tense of the verb **se lever** (to get up).

se	me	te	vous	nous

Je <u>me</u> lève   Nous <u>nous</u> levons
Tu <u>te</u> lèves   Vous <u>vous</u> levez
Il/Elle <u>se</u> lève   Ils/Elles <u>se</u> lèvent

2 Draw lines to match the French sentences about your daily routine to their English translation.

Je me lève. — I wake up.
Je me réveille. — I get dressed.
Je me peigne. — I get up.
Je me douche. — I comb my hair.
Je me couche. — I brush my teeth.
Je m'habille. — I have a shower.
Je me brosse les dents. — I go to bed.
Je prends le déjeuner. — I read a book.
Je lis un livre. — I have lunch.

45

3 Write the English for these French adverbs. **Note:** You may use a dictionary to help you.

normalement — normally
souvent — often
de temps en temps — from time to time
rarement — seldom

4 Complete the following sentences by adding an adverb to say how often you do the after-school activities mentioned. Answers may vary.

Je lis ....
Je sors avec mes copains ....
Je regarde la télé ....
Je fais mes devoirs ....
J'écoute de la musique ....

5 Read the paragraph in French below. Underline the time-connective words and phrases.

<u>Premièrement</u>, je me réveille. Je me lève <u>d'habitude</u> cinq minutes plus tard. <u>Puis</u>, je me lave, je m'habille et je prends mon petit déjeuner. <u>Après ça</u>, je me brosse les dents. <u>Finalement</u>, je me peigne.

Explain that reflexive verbs describe actions done to oneself. Many reflexive verbs are **–er** verbs. They follow the same rules as other **–er** verbs for conjugation, but they also have a reflexive pronoun (**se**). In front of a vowel or silent "h", **me**, **te** and **se** become **m'**, **t'** and **s'**.

46

1 Fill the gaps on the chart below. Use a dictionary to look up new words.

French	English	French	English
un pantalon	some trousers	une chemise	a shirt
un jean	some jeans	une robe	a dress
un tee-shirt	a T-shirt	une jupe	a skirt
un chemisier	a blouse	une écharpe	a scarf
un manteau	a coat	des gants	some gloves
un chapeau	a hat	des chaussettes	some socks
un pyjama	some pyjamas	des chaussures	some shoes
un short	some shorts	des sandales	some sandals

2 Discover what people are wearing by using the code-breaking key to decipher the sentences below.

e = ♠   u = ♥   o = ♣   s = ♦   t = ☼

J♠ p♣r♦♠ ♥n♠ v♠♦♦♠ ♠♦ ♥n j♠an.
Jo porte une veste et un jean.

♠v♠ p♣r♦♠ ♥n♠ j♥p♠ ♠♦ ♥n ch♠mi♦i♠r.
Eve porte une jupe et un chemisier.

☼♣m p♣r♦♠ ♥n ♦h♣r♣ ♠♦ ♥n ☼♠♠-♦hir♣.
Tom porte un short et un tee-shirt.

47

3 In each box, draw a picture of the garment described in French. Drawings may vary.

| une écharpe rouge à pois | une robe rose à carreaux | un tee-shirt blanc à rayures vertes | une jupe bleue à fleurs |

4 Finish these sentences. Note the use of the past tense (**j'ai porté**/I wore) and the near future tense (**je vais porter**/I am going to wear).

Aujourd'hui, je porte .... Answers may vary. ....
Hier, j'ai porté .... Answers may vary. ....
Demain, je vais porter .... Answers may vary. ....

5 Complete these sentences by describing what outfit you will wear.

Pour aller en ville, je vais porter .... Answers may vary. ....
Pour aller à la plage, je vais porter .... Answers may vary. ....

Describing clothes will give your child lots of opportunities to practise adjectival agreement. Encourage your child to refer back to pages 18–19 and 22–23. Also remind him or her that colours need to follow the noun. On these pages your child is also introduced to the past tense **j'ai porté** and the near future tense **je vais porter**.

Answers:

48–49 Quel temps fait-il?
50–51 A l'école

48

① Fill in the missing letters in the French descriptions of the weather symbols. **Note:** You may use a dictionary to help you.

Il pl**e**u**t**.

Il f**a**it nu**a**ge**u**x.

Il n**e**i**g**e.

Il **y** a des orages.

Il f**a**it cha**u**d.

Il **f**ait du ve**n**t.

Il fai**t** f**r**oid.

Il **f**ait du sol**e**i**l**.

② Describe the weather during the different seasons of the year by filling in the gaps in these sentences. The first one has been done for you.

En hiver, ___il neige___ et ___il fait froid___ .

Au printemps, ___Answers may vary.___ et ___Answers may vary.___ .

En été, ___Answers may vary.___ et ___Answers may vary.___ .

En automne, ___Answers may vary.___ et ___Answers may vary.___ .

49

③ Complete these sentences, writing what you would wear for the weather described.   Answers may vary.

Quand il fait chaud, je porte _____ .

Quand il fait froid, je porte _____ .

Quand il pleut, je porte _____ .

④ Look at the weather symbols on the map. Then complete the sentences given below the map. The first one has been done for you.

Nord
Ouest ← → Est
Sud

Dans le nord, ___il fait froid___ .　Dans le nord-est, ___il pleut___ .

Dans l'ouest, ___il fait nuageux___ .　Dans l'est, ___il fait du vent___ .

Dans le sud, ___il fait du soleil___ .　Dans le sud-ouest, ___il fait chaud___ .

To consolidate learning, it would be useful for your child to write the date each day in French and, under the date, a phrase to describe the weather. By combining weather phrases with phrases to describe what they are wearing/ what they are going to wear, children begin to build lengthier and more interesting sentences.

50

① Fill in the gaps on the chart below, showing some of the subjects taught in school. **Note:** You may use a dictionary to help you.

French	English	French	English
les maths	maths	la religion	R.E.
le théâtre	drama	la technologie	D.T.
les sciences	science	l'histoire	history
le français	French	la géographie	geography
le dessin	drawing	la musique	music
le sport	sport	l'informatique	I.C.T.

② Translate these English sentences into French.

Sport is okay, but I hate maths.

___Le sport est ok, mais je déteste les maths.___

I also like geography, because it's interesting.

___J'aime aussi la géographie, parce que c'est intéressante.___

Drawing is my favourite subject and sport is great, too!

___Le dessin est ma matière préférée et le sport est aussi formidable!___

I like history, but drama is awful!

___J'aime l'histoire, mais le théâtre est moche!___

51

③ Say which school subjects you like and which you dislike by filling in the gaps in these sentences. **Note:** In French, any subject you mention must always have **le, la, l'** or **les** in front of it.   Answers may vary.

J'aime _____ parce que c'est _____ .

Je n'aime pas _____ parce que c'est _____ .

J'aime beaucoup _____ parce que c'est _____ .

Je déteste _____ parce que c'est _____ .

④ Translate these French expressions into English.

C'est formidable! ___It's great!___

C'est intéressant. ___It's interesting.___

C'est amusant. ___It's amusing.___

C'est super! ___It's great!___

C'est facile. ___It's easy.___

C'est ok. ___It's okay.___

C'est nul! ___It's rubbish!___

C'est moche. ___It's awful.___

C'est difficile. ___It's difficult.___

By working through these pages, children are introduced to a range of informal as well as formal phrases to express their opinion about school subjects. This will help them to use and understand French as it is really spoken.

These phrases can be adapted to a wide variety of situations. Encourage your child to use them to describe clothes, colours, food and hobbies.

Answers:

52–53 La musique
54–55 Les nombres 70–1 000

52

① Add the French translations of the English words to this chart, saying whether they are masculine or feminine nouns.

English	French	Masculine or Feminine
clarinet	clarinette	Feminine
saxophone	saxophone	Masculine
piano	piano	Masculine
guitar	guitare	Feminine
trumpet	trompette	Feminine
drums	batterie	Feminine
violin	violon	Masculine
cello	violoncelle	Masculine

② Translate these sentences into English.

J'aime la musique classique. ...... I like classical music. ......

J'aime beaucoup la musique pop. ...... I really like pop music. ......

J'adore la musique folklorique! ...... I love folk music! ......

J'aime aussi la musique de ballet. ...... I also like ballet music. ......

Je n'aime pas le rock! ...... I don't like rock music! ......

53

③ Translate these sentences into French. **Note:** To say that you play a musical instrument, you use the verb **jouer** (to play) + **de** + the name of the instrument. The first one has been done for you.

I play the saxophone. **Je joue du saxophone.**

She plays the clarinet. ...... Elle joue de la clarinette. ......

Do you play the piano? ...... Tu joues du piano? ......

He plays the violin. ...... Il joue du violon. ......

We play the trumpet. ...... Nous jouons de la trompette. ......

They play the drums. ...... Ils/Elles jouent de la batterie. ......

They play the guitar. ...... Ils/Elles jouent de la guitare. ......

④ Translate what these people are saying into English.

Je ne joue pas d'instrument, mais j'aime les concerts.

...... I don't play an instrument, but I like concerts. ......

Je ne joue pas d'instrument, mais j'adore chanter.

...... I don't play an instrument, but I like singing. ......

Je joue du violon dans un orchestre et je chante dans un chorale aussi.

...... I play the violin in an orchestra and I sing in a choir as well. ......

Your child needs to use the phrase **jouer de** to say that he or she plays a musical instrument. Compare against **jouer à** (pages 38-39), which is used to say that one plays a sport. Remind your child to select the correct form **du** or **de la** depending on whether that musical instrument is masculine or feminine.

54

① Write the French for these numbers. The maths given after each number should give you a clue.

70 (60 + 10) ...... soixante-dix ......
80 (4 x 20) ...... quatre-vingts ......
90 (4 x 20 + 10) ...... quatre-vingt-dix ......

② Write the French for these numbers. Remember that the French for 100 is **cent** and that you add an "s" to make it plural, as in **six cents** (600).

200 ...... deux cents ......   900 ...... neuf cents ......
300 ...... trois cents ......   700 ...... sept cents ......
500 ...... cinq cents ......   800 ...... huit cents ......

③ Reorder the numbers given below, starting with the smallest at the top.

vingt-huit	...... vingt-huit ......
soixante-trois	...... trente-deux ......
quatre-vingt-dix-sept	...... quarante et un ......
soixante-treize	...... soixante-trois ......
mille	...... soixante-treize ......
quatre-vingt-six	...... quatre-vingt-six ......
trente-deux	...... quatre-vingt-dix-sept ......
quarante et un	...... cent ......
cent	...... mille ......

55

④ Draw lines to match the numbers on the left with the number words on the right.

190 — cent trente-quatre
172 — cent quatre-vingt-trois
165 — cent quatre-vingt-dix
183 — cent soixante-douze
134 — cent soixante-cinq

⑤ Solve these sums. Give your answers first in digits and then in French.

trente et un + quarante = ... 71 .... soixante et onze ......
trente + cinquante-deux = ... 82 .... quatre-vingt-deux ......
quatre-vingt-dix + onze = ... 101 .... cent un ......

⑥ Write the French for each amount of money.

€ 30.80 ...... trente euros quatre-vingts ......
€ 200.78 ...... deux cents euros soixante-dix-huit ......
€ 86.43 ...... quatre-vingt-six euros quarante-trois ......
€ 282.17 ...... deux cent quatre-vingt-deux euros dix-sept ......
€ 120.00 ...... cent vingt euros ......

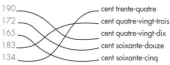

⑦ Write the year given below in French.

1971 ...... mille neuf cent soixante et onze ......

Make sure your child feels confident using numbers 1 to 21 first, as some larger numbers are built using these smaller numbers. The spelling of larger numbers can be tricky. Point out that **quatre-vingts** (80) with an "s" becomes **quatre-vingt-dix** (90) with no "s" after **vingt**. Similarly, **six cents** (600) with an "s" becomes **six cent quatre-vingt-deux** (682) with no "s" after cent.

Answers:

56–57 La nourriture et les boissons
58–59 Au café

56

① Fill in the French words on the chart. Remember to put **le**, **la**, **l'** or **les** before each one. **Note:** You may use a dictionary to help you.

English	French
rice	le riz
meat	la viande
pasta	les pâtes
bread	le pain
fruit	les fruits
cheese	le fromage
eggs	les œufs
butter	le beurre
fish	le poisson
soup	la soupe
vegetables	les légumes
potatoes	les pommes de terre
cake	le gâteau
ice-cream	la glace

② Unscramble the French sentences below. Then translate them into English.

du fromage? Veux-tu _Veux-tu du fromage?_ _Do you want some cheese?_

-tu Veux pain? du _Veux-tu du pain?_ _Do you want some bread?_

57

③ Unscramble these French words to reveal a list of drinks.

el tail _le lait_   l'aue _l'eau_

le afcé _le café_   el sju d'enroga _le jus d'orange_

le caoc _le coca_   el téh _le thé_

el toochlac _le chocolat_   al melanodi _la limonade_

④ Complete these sentences, using the correct French translation of the English word given in brackets.

Vous avez _du riz_ ? (rice)   Je vais prendre _des céréales_ . (cereals)

Vous avez _de l'huile_ ? (oil)   Je vais prendre _de la confiture_ . (jam)

⑤ Fill in the gaps in these sentences to describe what you usually eat in a day. Answers may vary.

Pour mon petit déjeuner, je mange _____
_____. Je bois _____.

Pour mon déjeuner, je mange _____
_____. Je bois _____.

Pour mon dîner, je mange _____
_____. Je bois _____.

On these pages, your child will practise offering food at the table and asking for food items in shops. For all of these sentences, your child will need to decide if the food is masculine, feminine or plural and select the right form – **du**, **de la**, **de l'** or **des**. He or she can also practise the useful phrases **j'aime** and **je n'aime pas** to express a preference. For example, **j'aime le jus d'orange**.

58

① Look at the French words for various popular snacks and drinks in the box below. Then find them in the word-search puzzle.

paquet de chips	orangina	tranche de pizza	coca
glace	portion de frites	hot-dog	hamburger
chocolat chaud	pain	sandwich au fromage	milkshake

s	z	t	r	a	n	c	h	e	d	e	p	i	z	z	a	h
a	d	a	s	d	f	g	h	j	k	l	a	w	f	r	y	p
n	v	c	u	a	i	o	q	p	h	j	q	z	p	w	m	o
d	b	d	h	o	t	-	d	o	g	v	u	x	p	d	l	r
w	n	e	k	x	u	p	e	o	f	c	e	c	a	c	p	t
i	m	t	y	s	y	k	w	u	y	r	t	v	i	v	o	i
c	d	g	h	r	t	l	y	i	q	w	d	b	n	f	i	o
h	a	m	b	u	r	g	e	r	b	m	e	r	k	r	i	n
a	e	i	a	s	f	g	h	j	k	l	c	t	g	t	u	e
u	t	l	z	c	v	x	b	n	m	l	h	y	o	g	u	e
f	y	k	c	o	g	l	a	c	e	m	i	u	r	b	j	f
r	u	s	v	i	q	r	f	o	v	b	p	i	a	n	m	r
o	i	h	d	u	a	d	h	c	d	a	s	o	n	y	t	i
m	o	a	e	h	z	e	o	a	u	i	j	k	g	w	r	t
a	p	k	z	x	c	v	b	g	t	c	v	b	i	n	m	e
g	y	e	q	w	e	r	t	y	u	i	i	o	n	p	k	s
e	r	i	c	h	o	c	o	l	a	t	c	h	a	u	d	c

59

② Translate these sentences into English.

Le menu, s'il vous plaît? _Could we have the menu, please?_

Vous avez choisi? _Are you ready to order?_

Vous désirez? _What would you like?_

L'addition, s'il vous plaît? _Could I have the bill, please?_

③ Unscramble these food orders.

une s'il frites, Je plaît. vous portion de voudrais
Je voudrais une portion de frites, s'il vous plaît.

fromage, Je plaît. s'il sandwich voudrais au un vous
Je voudrais un sandwich au fromage, s'il vous plaît.

voudrais Je de tranche une s'il pizza, vous plaît.
Je voudrais une tranche de pizza, s'il vous plaît.

milkshake, vous plaît. un Je s'il voudrais
Je voudrais un milkshake, s'il vous plaît.

④ Draw lines to match these ice-cream flavours with their English translations.

une glace au chocolat — a strawberry ice-cream
une glace au cassis — a vanilla ice-cream
une glace à la fraise — a blackcurrant ice-cream
une glace à la vanille — a chocolate ice-cream

Here your child can practise ordering food and drink in a polite way. As well as speaking, it is important that children get used to understanding phrases they might hear in a shop or café. Point out to your child that when ordering ice-cream, the flavour follows the noun.

Answers:

60–61 Le corps
62–63 Les vacances
64–65 Beat the clock 3, see p.80

60

1. Fill in the missing letters in these French words for parts of the body. **Note:** You may use a dictionary to help you.

les br a s   le d o s   les orei l les   la go r ge

les ma i ns   le co u   la bou c he   les épa u les

les ye u x   la tê t e   les jam b es   les ge n oux

2. Look at the monkey. Add numbers to the list next to it to say how many of each body part the monkey has.

deux oreilles   un dos

deux yeux   une bouche

deux mains   deux pieds

deux jambes   un nez

deux bras   une tête

un ventre   une queue

3. J'ai mal à... can be translated as "I have a pain in...". Choose the right preposition (**au**, **à la**, **à l'**, **aux**) to complete these sentences about bodily aches and pains.

J'ai mal aux dents.   J'ai mal au ventre.

J'ai mal aux yeux.   J'ai mal à la tête.

J'ai mal à l' oreille.   J'ai mal au dos.

61

4. Find the French word for each English clue to complete the crossword puzzle below.

Across
1. stomach ventre
2. fingers doigts
3. nose nez
4. ears oreilles
5. eyes yeux

Down
1. mouth bouche
2. hands mains
3. body corps
4. knees genoux
5. feet pieds
6. teeth dents
7. legs jambes

To say that something hurts, your child can practise using the structure **j'ai mal à** + a body part. Remind him or her that she will need to choose the right form **au**, **à la** or **aux** depending on whether the body part is masculine, feminine or plural. Your child must use **à l'** in front of a vowel.

62

1. Translate these sentences into French. **Note:** You need to use the correct form of **avoir** + **voyagé** to write your answers.

I travelled by plane.   J'ai voyagé en avion.

He travelled by car.   Il a voyagé en voiture.

We travelled by boat.   Nous avons voyagé en bateau.

2. Translate these sentences into French. **Note:** You need to use the correct form of **être** + **allé(e)(s)** to write your answers.

Pierre went to Italy.   Pierre est allé en Italie.

Sophie went to France.   Sophie est allée en France.

My sisters went to Africa.   Mes sœurs sont allées en Afrique.

My parents went to Portugal.   Mes parents sont allés au Portugal.

3. Choose the correct form of **avoir** or **être** to complete these sentences.

Nous sommes allés à une église.

Il a visité des monuments.

Elles sont allées à la plage.

Tu as fait de la rando?

J' ai acheté des souvenirs.

63

4. Here are some useful French expressions to help you say what you thought about some of the things you did on holiday. Draw lines to match them to their English translations.

C'était marrant.   It was dull.
C'était barbant.   It was frightening.
C'était rapide.   It was great!
C'était passionnant!   It was funny.
C'était terrifiant.   It was fast.
C'était chouette!   It was exciting!

5. You may have visited an amusement park while on holiday. Choose the correct form of **avoir** + **vu** to complete these sentences and say what your family saw on the ghost-train ride. Then write the English translation.

Ma sœur a vu un loup-garou.
My sister saw a werewolf.

Mon frère a vu un vampire.
My brother saw a vampire.

Mes parents ont vu des araignées.
My parents saw some spiders.

J' ai vu un squelette.
I saw a skeleton.

Explain to your child that the **l'imparfait** is used to talk about ongoing events or in descriptions, while the **le passé composé** is used to talk about events that occur once. Also, with **le passé composé**, your child needs to begin to think about when to use **avoir** and when to use **être**. It is helpful to know that **être** is generally used for verbs of movement. For example, **elles sont allées à la plage**.

Answers:

20 / 21

Je (parler) parle	Nous (aimer) aimons	Il (parler) parle	Elles (parler) parlent
Elle (arriver) arrive	Vous (parler) parlez	Je (donner) donne	Ils (parler) parlent
Tu (donner) donnes	Je (regarder) regarde	Nous (donner) donnons	Nous (habiter) habitons
Il (habiter) habite	Tu (regarder) regardes	Il (donner) donne	Vous (donner) donnez
Il (arriver) arrive	Il (travailler) travaille	Tu (arriver) arrives	Je (travailler) travaille
Tu (parler) parles	Il (jouer) joue	Elle (aimer) aime	Elle (regarder) regarde
Nous (parler) parlons	Tu (jouer) joues	Vous (habiter) habitez	Il (écouter) écoute
Vous (manger) mangez	Tu (écouter) écoutes	Elle (parler) parle	Nous (jouer) jouons
Ils (donner) donnent	Elle (donner) donne	Il (aimer) aime	Ils (aimer) aiment
Ils (arriver) arrivent	Tu (travailler) travailles	Vous (arriver) arrivez	Il (manger) mange
Elle (habiter) habite	Nous (écouter) écoutons	Il (regarder) regarde	Elles (donner) donnent
Ils (habiter) habitent	Vous (aimer) aimez	Elles (aimer) aiment	Vous (écouter) écoutez
Je (manger) mange	Elles (habiter) habitent	Elle (jouer) joue	Nous (arriver) arrivons
Tu (aimer) aimes	Je (jouer) joue	Tu (habiter) habites	Elles (arriver) arrivent

42 / 43

Je (choisir) choisis	Elle (réussir) réussit	Il (choisir) choisit	Je (réfléchir) réfléchis
Tu (finir) finis	Il (réfléchir) réfléchit	Nous (finir) finissons	Il (finir) finit
Il (réussir) réussit	Tu (choisir) choisis	Tu (réussir) réussis	Elle (remplir) remplit
Nous (choisir) choisissons	Je (finir) finis	Vous (réfléchir) réfléchissez	Elle (choisir) choisit
Ils (finir) finissent	Ils (réussir) réussissent	Il (remplir) remplit	Vous (réussir) réussissez
Elle (réfléchir) réfléchit	Ils (réfléchir) réfléchissent	Il (avertir) avertit	Elles (remplir) remplissent
Je (remplir) remplis	Tu (remplir) remplis	Elle (vieillir) vieillit	Tu (réfléchir) réfléchis
Nous (remplir) remplissons	Vous (choisir) choisissez	Elles (choisir) choisissent	Ils (choisir) choisissent
J' (avertir) avertis	Tu (avertir) avertis	Nous (réfléchir) réfléchissons	Vous (finir) finissez
Il (obéir) obéit	Il (vieillir) vieillit	Tu (obéir) obéis	Elle (avertir) avertit
Tu (vieillir) vieillis	Tu (établir) établis	Il (établir) établit	Nous (vieillir) vieillissons
Elle (finir) finit	J' (obéir) obéis	Ils (remplir) remplissent	Il (obéir) obéit
Nous (établir) établissons	Vous (remplir) remplissez	Elles (finir) finissent	Vous (établir) établissez
Elles (réfléchir) réfléchissent	Je (réussir) réussis	Nous (réussir) réussissons	Elles (réussir) réussissent

64 / 65

Je (decendre) descends	Elle (vendre) vend	Il (decendre) descend	J' (attendre) attends
Tu (perdre) perds	Il (attendre) attend	Nous (perdre) perdons	Il (perdre) perd
Il (vendre) vend	Tu (decendre) descends	Tu (vendre) vends	Elle (entendre) entend
Nous (decendre) descendons	Je (perdre) perds	Vous (attendre) attendez	Elle (descendre) descend
Ils (perdre) perdent	Ils (vendre) vendent	Il (entendre) entend	Vous (vendre) vendez
Elle (attendre) attend	Ils (attendre) attendent	Il (rendre) rend	Elles (entendre) entendent
J' (entendre) entends	Tu (entendre) entends	Elle (étendre) étend	Tu (attendre) attends
Nous (entendre) entendons	Vous (decendre) descendez	Elles (decendre) descendent	Ils (decendre) descendent
Je (rendre) rends	Tu (rendre) rends	Nous (attendre) attendons	Vous (perdre) perdez
Il (répondre) répond	Il (étendre) étend	Tu (répondre) réponds	Elle (rendre) rend
Tu (étendre) étends	Tu (pendre) pends	Il (pendre) pend	Nous (étendre) étendons
Elle (perdre) perd	Je (répondre) réponds	Ils (entendre) entendent	Il (répondre) répond
Nous (pendre) pendons	Vous (entendre) entendez	Elles (perdre) perdent	Vous (pendre) pendez
Elles (attendre) attendent	Je (vendre) vends	Nous (vendre) vendons	Elles (vendre) vendent

These "Beat the clock" pages test your child's ability to quickly recall the lessons learned. The tests require your child to work under some pressure. As with most tests of this type, tell your child before he or she starts not to get stuck on one question, but to move on and return to the tricky one later if time allows. Encourage your child to record his or her score and the time taken to complete the test. You can also encourage your child to retake the test later to see if he or she can improve on his or her previous attempt.